LINES AND SURFACES IN AFFINE THREE-DIMENTIONAL SPACE

Lines and Surfaces
in
Three-Dimensional Affine Space

L. K. Tutaev

Israel Program for Scientific Translations
Jerusalem 1964

Published in the U. S. A. by:
DANIEL DAVEY & CO., INC.
257 Park Avenue South, New York, N. Y.

This book is a translation of
LINII I POVERKHNOSTI V AFFINNOM
TREKHMERNOM PROSTRANSTVE

Izdatel'stvo
Ministerstva vysshego, srednego spetsial'nogo
i professional'nogo obrazovaniya BSSR
Minsk 1962

Translated and Edited by
IPST Staff

IPST Cat. No. 2086

Printed in Israel by S. Monson, Jerusalem

CONTENTS

Part Two
LINES IN SPACE

FOREWORD

The differential geometry of lines and surfaces in equiaffine three-dimensional space was constructed by W. Blaschke /1/. An exposition of the method for investigating nonmetric spaces by means of tensor analysis is given in A. P. Norden's book /2/.

P. A. Shirokov and A. P. Shirokova's book containing the principal divisions of the differential geometry of the equiaffine, centroaffine and equicentroaffine groups came out in 1959 /3/. It includes an extensive bibliography relating to affine differential geometry. The same year saw the publication of a book by R. N. Shcherbakov in which the equiaffine geometry of lines and surfaces in three-dimensional space is treated by the method of exterior forms /4/.

A more complete investigation of the equiaffine differential geometry of lines, surfaces and congruences of straight lines by Shcherbakov was published in 1960.

The present monograph gives an exposition of the differential geometry of lines and surfaces of the affine group with the aid of the method of exterior forms. Particular stress is laid on elucidation of the geometric meaning of differential invariants.

The author expresses his gratitude to V. I. Platonova for reading the manuscript and for valuable advice.

INTRODUCTION

§ 1. Affine space. In a three-dimensional affine space a "frame" [Fr. repère] is provided by a triad of noncoplanar vectors with a common origin. In the frame $(A, \bar{e}_1, \bar{e}_2, \bar{e}_3)$ with origin at the point A and coordinate vectors $\bar{e}_1, \bar{e}_2, \bar{e}_3$, the radius vector $\overline{AX}$ of any point X in the given space can be expressed as a linear combination of the coordinate vectors:

$$\overline{AX}=x^1\bar{e}_1+x^2\bar{e}_2+x^3\bar{e}_3,$$

or, briefly,

$$\overline{AX} = x^i\bar{e}_i \quad (i = 1, 2, 3). \tag{1.1}$$

The numbers x^i are the coordinates of the point X in the frame $(A, \bar{e}_1, \bar{e}_2, \bar{e}_3)$. A point transformation in space is called affine if to any point X (x^i) there corresponds a point Y (y^i) such that

$$y^i = c^i_k x^k + c^i \quad (i, k = 1, 2, 3), \tag{1.2}$$

$$det\,|c^i_k| \neq 0. \tag{1.3}$$

The set of all affine transformations in three-dimensional space can again be expressed in the form of equations (1.2) subject to the condition (1.3), except that the symbols c^i_k, c^i will denote parameters. The set of all affine transformations forms a group. This group will be of twelve parameters, the number of independent parameters c^i_k, c^i.

A space consisting of the points X (x^1, x^2, x^3) with the radius vectors (1.1) and affine transformations (1.2–1.3) is called a three-dimensional affine space. An affine surface can be defined analogously as a two-dimensional affine space.

§ 2. Pfaffian forms. A linear form

$$b_1da^1 + b_2da^2 + \ldots + b_rda^r$$

in the differentials $da^1, da^2, da^3, \ldots, da^r$ with coefficients $b_1, b_2, b_3, \ldots, b_r$, dependent on the variables $a^1, a^2, a^3, \ldots, a^r$, is called a Pfaffian form.

Let us denote it by the symbol ω and write, briefly:

$$\omega = b_ida^i. \qquad (i = 1,2,\ldots,r)$$

By the rank of the system of Pfaffian forms

$$\omega^\alpha = b^\alpha_i da^i \qquad (\alpha = 1,2,\ldots,s) \tag{2.1}$$

is meant the rank of the matrix $\|b^\alpha_i\|$. This means that the rank m of the system (2.1) equals the maximum number of linearly independent $b^\alpha_i da^i$.

Let $\omega^1, \omega^2, \ldots, \omega^m$ be such forms; then all forms of the system (2.1) will be linear combinations of the latter. The set of all forms which are linear combinations of $\omega^1, \omega^2, \ldots, \omega^m$ is called a ring of forms with basis $\omega^1, \omega^2, \ldots, \omega^m$ over the field P if the coefficients of the linear combinations belong to the field P. Any m linearly independent forms of this ring can be taken as its basis over the same field P.

§ 3. Grassmann ring. The elements α, β, γ belong to a field P. Other element-vectors $u, v, w, \ldots$, constituting the set L exist over the field P. The elements of the set L form a vector space over the field P.

There exists an operation called addition of vectors by which, given two arbitrary vectors u and v, one obtains the vector $u+v$ which is called the sum of u and v; there exists another operation called multiplication of an element of the field P by a vector u, which gives the vector αu, the product of the element α by the vector u. These operations satisfy the following requirements.

1. The addition of vectors is commutative;

$$u + v = v + u.$$

2. The addition of vectors is associative:

$$u + (v + w) = (u + v) + w.$$

3. Subtraction of vectors is possible, i.e., for every two vectors u, v there exists a vector x in the same set L such that

$$u + x = v.$$

4. Multiplication of the element α of the field P by the vector u is commutative:

$$\alpha u = u\alpha.$$

5. Multiplication of the element 1 of the field P by the vector u satisfies the condition

$$1 \cdot u = u.$$

6. Multiplication is associative:

$$\alpha (\beta u) = (\alpha\beta) u.$$

7. Multiplication is distributive with respect to addition of vectors:

$$\alpha (u + v) = \alpha u + \alpha v.$$

8. Multiplication is distributive with respect to addition of elements of the field P:

$$(\alpha + \beta) u = \alpha u + \beta u.$$

There exists an operation called exterior multiplication of the vectors $u_1, u_2, \ldots, u_p$, by which one obtains the exterior product of these vectors $[u_1\ u_2 \ldots u_p]$. Here the square brackets denote exterior multiplication.

The element α of the field P can be multiplied by the exterior product $[u_1\ u_2 \ldots u_p]$. By this multiplication we obtain the product $\alpha[u_1\ u_2 \ldots u_p]$, called a monomial of degree p. The degree of the monomial is equal to the number of vectors in the exterior product. Addition and exterior multiplication can be performed on monomials. The indicated operations on the vectors

u, v, ..., the monomials U, V, W, ... and the elements α, β, ... of the field P satisfy the following conditions.

1. The exterior multiplication of two vectors is anticommutative:

$$[uv] = -[vu].$$

2. The multiplication of an element of the field P by an exterior product of two vectors satisfies

$$\alpha[uv] = [\alpha u, v].$$

3. The exterior multiplication of monomials is associative:

$$[U[VW]] = [[UV]W].$$

4. Multiplication is distributive with respect to addition of monomials:

$$[U+V, \ W] = [UW] + [VW];$$

$$[U, \ V+W] = [UV] + [UW].$$

Let us note a few corollaries of the requirements 1-8 and 1-4.

Corollary 1. The interchange of any two factors multiplies a monomial by -1.

Corollary 2. A monomial with two equal factors equals zero.

§ 4. Cartan's ring. We have the field of all analytic functions of n variables x^1, x^2, ..., x^n.

We add to it all the differentials dx^1, dx^2, ..., dx^n. By the exterior differential form of degree p is meant the form

$$\Omega = a_{i_1 i_2 \cdots i_p}[dx^{i_1}, dx^{i_2}, \ldots, dx^{i_p}] \quad (i_1, i_2, \ldots, i_p = 1, 2, \ldots, n). \tag{4.1}$$

The square brackets indicate exterior multiplication of the differentials $dx^{i_1}, dx^{i_2}, \ldots, dx^{i_p}$, and the coefficients $a_{i_1 i_2 \cdots i_p}$ are functions of the variables $x^1, x^2, \ldots, x^n$ of the given field; the summation over each index $i_1, \ldots, i_p$ is independent of the summations over the remaining indices.

By the adjoint form of Ω is meant the form

$$\Omega(d_1, d_2, \ldots, d_p) = a_{i_1 i_2 \cdots i_p} \begin{vmatrix} d_1x^1 d_1x^2, \ldots, d_1x^p \\ d_2x^1 d_2x^2, \ldots, d_2x^p \\ \cdots\cdots\cdots\cdots \\ d_px^1 d_px^2, \ldots, d_px^p \end{vmatrix}, \tag{4.2}$$

where $(d_1x^1, \ldots, d_1x^p)$, $(d_2x^1, \ldots, d_2x^p)$, ..., $(d_px^1, \ldots, d_px^p)$ are the sets of numerical values of the differentials $(dx^1, \ldots, dx^p)$.

Cartan's lemma. If the $2r$ linear forms ω^i and Θ_i $(i = 1, 2, \ldots, r)$ of $n \geqslant r$ variables are related by

$$[\omega^1\Theta_1] + [\omega^2\Theta_2] + \ldots + [\omega^p\Theta_p] = \Theta \tag{4.3}$$

and the forms ω^i are linearly independent, then the forms Θ_i are linear combinations of the forms ω^i with symmetric coefficients:

$$\Theta_i = c_{ij}\omega^j, \qquad (i, j = 1, 2, \ldots, r); \tag{4.4}$$

$$c_{ij} = c_{ji}. \tag{4.5}$$

T h e o r e m 1. If s Pfaffian forms are linearly dependent then their exterior product vanishes, and, conversely, if the exterior product of the Pfaffian forms vanishes then the forms are linearly dependent.

§ 5. Exterior differentiation. By the exterior differential of the exterior differential form of degree p

$$\Omega = a_{i_1 \dots i_p} [dx^{i_1} \dots dx^{i_p}]$$

is meant the exterior differential form of degree $p+1$:

$$D\Omega = [da_{i_1 \dots i_p} dx^{i_1} \dots dx^{i_p}] = \frac{\partial a_{i_1 \dots i_p}}{\partial x^{i_{p+1}}} [dx^{i_{p+1}} dx^{i_1} \dots dx^{i_p}]. \qquad (5.1)$$

Henceforth the symbol $D\Omega$ will denote the exterior differential of the form Ω.

The rules of exterior differentiation follow from the definition of the exterior differential:

$$D(\Omega^1 + \Omega^2) = D\Omega^1 + D\Omega^2, \qquad (5.2)$$

$$D(m\Omega) = mD\Omega + [dm\Omega], \qquad (5.3)$$

if m is a function of the variables $x^1, x^2, \dots, x^n$;

$$D[\Omega_p, \Omega_q] = [D\Omega_p, \Omega_q] + (-1)^p [D\Omega_q, \Omega_p], \qquad (5.4)$$

where p, q are the degrees of the forms Ω_p and Ω_q.

The following theorems hold.

T h e o r e m 1. The exterior differential of the total differential of a function vanishes, and conversely, if the exterior differential of a Pfaffian form vanishes, then this form is the total differential of a function.

T h e o r e m 2. The exterior differential of the exterior differential of any exterior differential form vanishes.

§ 6. Pfaffian system of differential equations. If $\Theta_1, \Theta_2, \dots, \Theta_p$ are Pfaffian forms, then the equations

$$\Theta_1 = 0; \ \Theta_2 = 0, \dots, \Theta_p = 0 \qquad (6.1)$$

form a Pfaffian system of differential equations.

If all the Pfaffian forms

$$\Theta_\alpha = a_{\alpha i} dx^i \qquad (\alpha = 1, 2, \dots, p; \ i = 1, 2, \dots, n; \ n > p)$$

are linearly independent and, say, the rank of the matrix

$$\begin{Vmatrix} a_{11} \, a_{12} \dots a_{1p} \\ \dots\dots\dots\dots \\ a_{p1} \, a_{p2} \dots a_{pp} \end{Vmatrix}$$

is p, then the system of equations (6.1) can be solved for

$$dx^1, dx^2, \dots, dx^p.$$

The Pfaffian system of differential equations (6.1) is called completely integrable if the system of equations obtained from the system (6.1) by exterior differentiation

$$D\Theta_1 = 0; \ D\Theta_2 = 0, \dots, D\Theta_p = 0, \qquad (6.2)$$

is an algebraic corollary of the system (6.1).

The system (6.2) is an algebraic corollary of the system (6.1) if, upon introducing the expressions for the differentials $dx^1, \dots, dx^p$ obtained from (6.1) into the equations (6.2), the latter are identically satisfied.

§ 7. Moving frame [Fr. repère mobile]. If $d\overline{A}$, $d\overline{e_1}$, $d\overline{e_2}$, $d\overline{e_3}$ are respectively the differentials of the radius vector of the origin A and the coordinate vectors of the frame $(A, \overline{e_1}, \overline{e_2}, \overline{e_3})$ for infinitesimal displacements of the latter in three-dimensional affine space, then

$$d\overline{A} = \omega^i \overline{e_i}, \quad d\overline{e_i} = \omega_i^j \overline{e_j} \qquad (i, j = 1, 2, 3), \tag{7.1}$$

where ω^i, ω_i^j are Pfaffian forms dependent on the parameters of the group of affine transformations.

These forms are called components of the infinitesimal displacements of the frame.

The equations (7.1) are a Pfaffian system of differential equations. If here the parameters of the group of affine transformations (or the variables on which these parameters depend) are regarded as independent variables and the vectors $\overline{A}$, $\overline{e_1}$, $\overline{e_2}$, $\overline{e_3}$ as unknowns, then the system (7.1) has as many unknowns as equations.

The system of equations (7.1) is completely integrable (§ 6) if the system of equations obtained from it by exterior differentiation is an algebraic corollary of (7.1).

Using once more equations (7.1), theorem 1 of § 5, formulas (5.2) and (5.3) and the linear independence of the vectors $\overline{e_1}$, $\overline{e_2}$, $\overline{e_3}$, we obtain by exterior differentiation of equations (7.1), the conditions of complete integrability of the system (7.1):

$$D\omega^i = \left[\omega^j \omega_j^i\right], \quad D\omega_i^j = \left[\omega_i^k \omega_k^j\right]. \tag{7.2}$$

These equations are called the structure equations of the system (7.1).

§ 8. System of exterior differential equations. We have Cartan's ring with the basis $(dx^1, \dots, dx^n;\ dz^1, \dots, dz^r)$ and the system of exterior differential equations

$$\Theta^{\alpha_p} \equiv a^{\alpha_p}_{i_1 \dots i_u j_1 \dots j_v} \left[dx^{i_1} \cdots dx^{i_u} \text{ and } dz^{j_1} \cdots dz^{j_v}\right] = 0 \tag{8.1}$$

$$(p = 1, \dots, m;\ \alpha_1 = 1, \dots, \beta_1;\ \alpha_2 = 1, \dots, \beta_2;\ \dots;\ \alpha_m = 1, \dots, \beta_m),$$

in which $x^1, \dots, x^n$ are independent variables, $z^1, \dots, z^r$ the required functions, $a^{\alpha_p}_{i_1 \dots i_u j_1 \dots j_v}$ are functions of $x^1, \dots, x^n;\ z^1, \dots, z^r$ and

$$u + v = p. \tag{8.2}$$

Aside from the exterior differential equations (8.1), one can give equations in a finite form:

$$F^{\alpha_0}(x^1, \dots, x^n;\ z^1, \dots, z^r) = 0 \qquad (\alpha_0 = 1, \dots, \beta_0). \tag{8.3}$$

If one adds to the system of equations (8.1) all equations obtained by exterior differentiation of the given equations,

$$D\Theta^{\alpha_p} = 0, \tag{8.4}$$

then the system of equations (8.1), (8.4) will be closed with respect to exterior differentiation /6/. Collecting together all equations of the first degree (Pfaffian equations), all equations of the second degree, etc. from the system of equations (8.1), (8.4), we obtain in general $m+1$ systems of exterior differential equations:

$$A^{\alpha_1}=0; \quad A^{\alpha_2}=0, \ldots, A^{\alpha_{m+1}}=0; \tag{8.5}$$

$$(\alpha_1=1, \ldots, \gamma_1; \ \alpha_2=1, \ldots, \gamma_2; \ \alpha_{m+1}=1, \ldots, \gamma_{m+1}). \tag{8.6}$$

If

$$\gamma_1<r$$

and s_1 is the rank of the system

$$A^{\alpha_1}=0 \qquad (\alpha_1=1, \ldots, \gamma_1) \tag{8.7}$$

of equations in $dz^1, \ldots, dz^r$, then, corresponding to a fixed point M $(x^1, \ldots, x^n; z^1 \ldots, z^r)$ one can assign arbitrarily the values of the differentials $d_1x^1, \ldots, d_1x^n$; $d_1z^1, \ldots, d_1z^{r-s_1}$, and solve the system (8.7) for $dz^{r-s_1+1}, \ldots, dz^r$ if the corresponding determinant is nonzero.

Let us obtain the set of numerical values of the differentials $(d_1x^1, \ldots, d_1x^n; d_1z^1, \ldots, d_1z^r)$ satisfying the system of equations (8.7) at the point M.

We will write these equations in the form

$$A^{\alpha_1}(d_1)=0 \qquad (\alpha_1=1, \ldots, s_1). \tag{8.8}$$

The point M and the set of values of the differentials $(d_1x^1, \ldots, d_1x^n; d_1z^1, \ldots, d_1z^r)$ satisfying the system of equations (8.8) is called the linear integral element of the system of equations (8.1), (8.4). We shall denote it by e_1. If we introduce the values corresponding to the linear integral element e_1 into the forms of second degree adjoint to the forms A^{α_2} of the system (8.8), then we will obtain a system of linear equations in the second set of differentials $d_2x^1, \ldots, d_2x^n$; $d_2z^1, \ldots, d_2z^r$ which we will write in the form

$$A^{\alpha_2}(d_1, d_2)=0 \qquad (\alpha_2=1, \ldots, \gamma_2). \tag{8.9}$$

If the rank of the system of equations (8.9) in $d_2z^1, \ldots, d_2z^r$ is s_2, then from this system and the first set of equations (8.5)

$$A^{\alpha_1}(d_2)=0 \qquad (\alpha_1=1, \ldots, s_1) \tag{8.10}$$

one can obtain $d_2z^{r-s_2+1}, \ldots, d_2z^r$ if the values of the differentials $d_2x^1, \ldots, d_2x^n$; $d_2z^1, \ldots, d_2z^{r-s_2}$ have been assigned and the corresponding determinant is nonzero. The point M and the set of values of the differentials $d_2x^1, \ldots, d_2x^n$; $d_2z^1, \ldots, d_2z^n$, linearly independent of $d_1x^1, \ldots, d_1x^n; d_1z^1, \ldots, d_1z$, which satisfy the equations (8.9–8.10) will be the second linear integral element of the system (8.1), (8.4), which we will denote by e_2. If, continuing in this manner, we obtain the linear integral elements $e_1, e_2, \ldots, e_{\nu-1}$, then the linear integral element e_ν will be obtained from the system of linear equations

$$A^{\alpha_1}(d_\nu)=0; \ A^{\alpha_2}(d_{\lambda_1}, d_\nu)=0; \ A^{\alpha_3}(d_{\lambda_1}, d_{\lambda_2}, d_\nu)=0 \ldots,$$

$$A^{\alpha_\nu}(d_1, d_2, \ldots, d_\nu)=0 \tag{8.10a}$$

$$(\lambda_1, \lambda_2, \ldots, \lambda_{\nu-1}=1, 2, \ldots, \nu-1).$$

The system of equations (8.10a) $(\nu=1,2, \ldots, n)$ is called the polar system corresponding to equations (8.1), (8.4). The point M $(x^i; z^j)$ $(i=1, \ldots, n;$ $j=1, \ldots, r)$ is said to be ordinary with respect to the system of equations (8.1), (8.4) if the ranks of the polar systems of equations (8.10a) at all points in its neighborhood are not higher than that for the point M. The ranks of the polar system of equations (8.10a), which correspond to the ordinary point M, are called the characters of this system.

Let us denote respectively by $s, s_1, \ldots, s_{\nu-1}$ the characters of the system of equations (8.10a). Once the linear integral element e_1 has been obtained the values of the differentials of the independent variables are given by $d_1 x^i$; s of the differentials of the unknown functions can be obtained from the system (8.8); consequently, the number of differentials of the unknown functions which may be assigned arbitrarily is given by

$$r_1 = r - s.$$

The number r_1 of free differentials of unknown functions upon choice of a linear integral element e_1 is called the characteristic number corresponding to this element.

To the sequence of linear integral elements e_1, e_2, e_ν there corresponds the sequence of characteristic numbers:

$$\left.\begin{array}{l} r_1 = r - s; \\ r_2 = r_1 - s_1 = r - (s + s_1); \\ r_3 = r_2 - s_2 = r - (s + s_1 + s_2); \\ \ldots\ldots\ldots\ldots\ldots\ldots\ldots\ldots\ldots\ldots\ldots \\ r_\nu = r_{\nu-1} - s_{\nu-1} = r - (s + s_1 + \ldots + s_{\nu-1}). \end{array}\right\} \quad (8.11)$$

The last nonzero characteristic number is also called the character /6/.

If this number is r_ν, then, denoting it by s_ν, we obtain

$$r = s + s_1 + s_2 + \ldots + s_\nu. \quad (8.12)$$

The ν-dimensional integral element of the system (8.1), (8.4) with reference to the point M is the set $e_1, e_2, \ldots, e_\nu$ of linear integral elements of this system with reference to the same point.

Let us denote it by E_ν. The integral elements referred to the point M will form a chain of integral elements

$$E_1 < E_2 < \ldots < E_\nu, \quad (8.13)$$

if each of these, except E_1, contains the preceding element. The integral element E_ν is nonsingular if the point M is ordinary. A chain of integral elements is regular if each of its elements is nonsingular.

§ 9. **Integral manifolds.** The criterion for the existence and composition of the integral manifold of a system of exterior differential equations is given in /6/.

Cartan's Theorem. If there exists a regular chain of integral elements (8.13) with characters (8.11–8.12), then through every point M there passes an integral line $(M)_1$, through every $(M)_1$ there passes a two-dimensional integral manifold $(M)_2$, and so on, through every $(M)_{p-1}$ there passes a p-dimensional integral manifold $(M)_p$, which is arbitrary to the extent of

s_p arbitrary functions of p arguments,
s_{p-1} " " $p-1$ " ,
s_1 " " 1 argument and s arbitrary constants.

The system of equations (8.1), (8.4) which satisfies this theorem is called an involutive system.

One is sometimes required to determine the existence and composition of the integral manifolds $(M)_p$ of the system (8.1), (8.4) if it is known that the Pfaffian forms $\omega^1, \ldots, \omega^n$ from the subring with the basis $(dx^1, \ldots, dx^n)$ are linearly independent and that the Pfaffian forms $\Theta^1, \ldots, \Theta^s$ tend to zero at $(M)_n$ and form a system of linearly independent forms together with $\omega^1, \ldots, \omega^n$. Let the Pfaffian forms $\widetilde{\omega}_q (q=1, \ldots, r-s)$ complement the forms $\omega^1, \ldots, \omega^n$, $\Theta^s, \ldots, \Theta^3$ to the basis of the ring. Then the existence and composition of the integral manifold $(M)_p$ of the system (8.1) can be determined by the following test /6/.

Cartan's test. Let the matrix of the indeterminate quantities $u^i_a (i, a = 1, \ldots, p)$ be arbitrary; correspondingly, let the ranks of the coefficient matrices (for unknown $\omega^{\overset{q}{\vee}}$) in the polar systems which define the integral elements E_ν $(\nu = 1, \ldots, p)$ of a chain be $\sigma_1 + \ldots + \sigma_\nu$. If the corresponding characters are $\sigma_1, \ldots, \sigma_p$, which satisfy the equation

$$\sigma_1 + 2\sigma_2 + \ldots + p\sigma_p = N,$$

where N is the arbitrariness of the most general p-dimensional integral element, then: the chain is regular; the system is involutive; the characters $S_a = \sigma_a$; and the arbitrariness of the integral manifold $(M)_p$ is given by Cartan's theorem.

Part One
LINES ON A PLANE

Chapter I

THE CANONICAL FRAME

§ 1. Fundamental relations. The equation of the line (A) on a plane in the frame $(O, \overline{u_1}, \overline{u_2})$ with origin O and coordinate vectors $\overline{u_1}, \overline{u_2}$ can be given in the form

$$\overline{OA} = x^1(t)\overline{u_1} + x^2(t)\overline{u_2}, \qquad (1.1)$$

where $\overline{OA}$ is the radius vector of the generic point A of this line, t is a parameter and $x^1(t), x^2(t)$ are the coordinates of the point A. If the point is the origin of the two noncollinear vectors $\overline{e_1}, \overline{e_2}$, then the frame $(A, \overline{e_1}, \overline{e_2})$ will refer to the point A. The equations for infinitesimal displacements of this frame in a plane (7.1, Introduction) are:

$$d\overline{A} = \omega^i \overline{e_i}; \quad d\overline{e_i} = \omega_i^j \overline{e_j} \qquad (i, j, n = 1,2). \qquad (1.2)$$

The equations of structure (7.2, Introduction) corresponding to this system are:

$$D\omega^i = \left[\omega^k \omega_k^i\right]; \quad D\omega_i^j = \left[\omega_i^k \omega_k^j\right]. \qquad (1.3)$$

Frames with origins at a fixed point A will be called frames of zero order with reference to this point.

§ 2. Frames of first order. Let us denote by $\overline{A}$ the radius vector $\overline{OA}$. The vector

$$d\overline{A} = u_1\, dx^1 + u_2\, dx^2, \qquad (2.1)$$

obtained from equation (1.1) will be the tangent to the line (A) at the point A. From the frames of zero order we choose one in which the vector $\overline{e_1}$ lies on the tangent to the line (A) at the point A. Therefore from the first equation in (1.2) we obtain

$$d\overline{A} = \omega^1 \overline{e_1}; \qquad (2.2)$$

$$\omega^2 = 0. \qquad (2.3)$$

The zero order frames $(A, \overline{e_1}, \overline{e_2})$ with vectors $\overline{e_1}$ lying on the tangent to the line (A) at the point A will be called frames of first order with reference to the line (A) and the point A. The condition (2.3) is necessary and sufficient to distinguish frames of first order.

This can be stated differently: with reference to frames of the first order equation (2.3) is the equation of the common axis of these frames.

To obtain equations for the line (A) expressed only in terms of quantities invariant under affine transformations, one must choose the frame $(A, \overline{e_1}, \overline{e_2})$ determined by the affine properties of the line (A) in the neighborhood of the point A.

Such a frame is termed canonical or normal. Supplementary conditions for its choice can be obtained by means of continuation of the initial equation (2.3), i.e., by means of exterior differentiation of this equation and a sequence of exterior differentiations of the resulting equations. The requirements contained in the structure equations (1.3) must be satisfied.

The form ω^1 cannot be identically zero since otherwise

$$d\bar{A} = 0,$$

would have been obtained from equation (2.2), which would have meant degeneration of the line (A) at the point A. An infinitesimal displacement $d\bar{A}=\omega^1\bar{e}_1$ of the point A on the line (A) will depend only on the form ω^1, here called the principal form.

The remaining forms ω^1_1, ω^2_1, ω^1_2, ω^2_2 depend on the latter for infinitesimal displacement of the canonical frame $(A, \bar{e}_1, \bar{e}_2)$; such forms ω^1_1, ω^2_1, ω^1_2, ω^2_2 are called secondary.

§ 3. Continuation of equation (2.3). Upon exterior differentiation of equation (2.3), we obtain

$$D\omega^2 = 0.$$

Consequently, according to the structure equation (1.3) and equation (2.3),

$$\left[\omega^1 \omega^2_1\right] = 0.$$

This means that the forms ω^1 and ω^2_1 are linearly dependent. Let us write this dependence in the form

$$\omega^2_1 = a^2_{11}\,\omega^1. \tag{3.1}$$

Upon exterior differentiation of equation (3.1) we obtain, using equations (1.3), (2.3) and simplifying,

$$\left[da^2_{11} - 2a^2_{11}\omega^1_1 + a^2_{11}\omega^2_2\omega^1\right] = 0.$$

Consequently,

$$da^2_{11} = 2a^2_{11}\omega^1_1 - a^2_{11}\omega^2_2 + a^2_{21}\omega^1. \tag{3.2}$$

Continuing equation (3.2), we obtain

$$\left.\begin{aligned} da^2_{21} &= 3a^2_{21}\omega^1_1 + 3a^2_{11}a^2_{11}\omega^1_2 - a^2_{21}\omega^2_2 + a^2_{31}\omega^1;\\ da^2_{31} &= 4a^2_{31}\omega^1_1 + 6a^2_{21}a^2_{11}\omega^1_2 + 4a^2_{11}a^2_{21}\omega^1_2 - a^2_{31}\omega^2_2 + a^2_{41}\omega^1.\end{aligned}\right\} \tag{3.3}$$

§ 4. Choice of the canonical frame. Let us assume that in equations (3.1–3.3)

$$a^2_{11} = 1; \qquad a^2_{21} = 0; \tag{4.1}$$

$$a^2_{31} = -3\varepsilon. \tag{4.2}$$

The quantity ε can take on the value + 1 or - 1. Correspondingly, the point A of the line (A) will be called a point of the hyperbolic or elliptic type. Let us set

$$k = \frac{a^2_{41}}{6\varepsilon}. \tag{4.3}$$

Consequently, equations (2.2) and (1.2 : 2) can be written in the form

$$d\overline{A} = \omega^1\overline{e_1}; \quad d\overline{e_1} = (k\overline{e_1} + \overline{e_2})\,\omega^1; \quad d\overline{e_2} = (\varepsilon\overline{e_1} + 2k\overline{e_2})\,\omega^1. \tag{4.4}$$

This determines the canonical frame at a point of the hyperbolic or elliptic type. We will call the quantity k the affine curvature of the line (A) at the point A. It can happen that, for the values given in equation (4.1),

$$a^2_{31} = 0. \tag{4.5}$$

Equations (2.2) and (1.2 : 2) then assume the form

$$d\overline{A} = \omega^1\overline{e_1}; \quad d\overline{e_1} = \omega^1_1\overline{e_1} + \omega^1\overline{e_2}; \quad d\overline{e_2} = 2\omega^1_1\overline{e_2}. \tag{4.6}$$

If the principal form ω^1 vanishes, the point A and coordinate axes become fixed and the coordinate vectors e_1 and e_2 form a one-parameter family. We set

$$\omega^1_1 = k\omega^1. \tag{4.7}$$

The quantity k in formula (4.7) is defined under the condition (4.5) and is different from the quantity k in formula (4.3), which was obtained under the condition (4.2). However, with the help of equation (4.7) equations (4.6) become formally identical with equations (4.4) for $\varepsilon = 0$.

We will make use of this fact and say that for $\varepsilon = 0$ equations (4.4) refer to a point of the parabolic type.

§ 5. Natural parameter. The exterior differential of the principal form is

$$D\omega^1 = [\omega^1 \cdot k\omega^1] \equiv 0.$$

Therefore one can set

$$\omega^1 = d\sigma. \tag{5.1}$$

The parameter σ will be called natural.

§ 6. Frenet-Cartan formulas. With the aid of equation (5.1) formulas (4.4) can be written in the form

$$\frac{d\overline{A}}{d\sigma} = \overline{e_1}; \quad \frac{d\overline{e_1}}{d\sigma} = k\overline{e_1} + \overline{e_2}; \quad \frac{d\overline{e_2}}{d\sigma} = \varepsilon\overline{e_1} + 2k\overline{e_2}. \tag{6.1}$$

The straight line passing through the point A of line (A) and containing the vector e_2 of the canonical frame (A, e_1, e_2) is called the affine normal to the line (A) at the point A.

§ 7. Equation of a line in its canonical frame. Let $A(\sigma)$ be an arbitrary point of the line (A) corresponding to the value σ of the natural parameter, x^1, x^2 be its coordinates in the canonical frame $(A, \overline{e_1}, \overline{e_2})$ and the origin A correspond to $\sigma = 0$. We have

$$\overline{AA}(\sigma) = x^1\overline{e_1} + x^2\overline{e_2}. \tag{7.1}$$

From Maclaurin's Theorem

$$\overline{AA}(\sigma) = d\overline{A} + \frac{1}{2}\,d^2\overline{A} + \frac{1}{6}d^3\overline{A} + \frac{1}{24}\,d^4\overline{A} + \frac{1}{120}\,d^5\overline{A} + \ldots \tag{7.2}$$

From formulas (6.1)

$$\left.\begin{aligned}
&\frac{d\overline{A}}{d\sigma}=\overline{e}_1;\quad \frac{d^2\overline{A}}{d\sigma^2}=k\overline{e}_1+\overline{e}_2;\quad \frac{d^3\overline{A}}{d\sigma^3}=(k'+k^2+\varepsilon)\overline{e}_1+3k\overline{e}_2;\\
&\frac{d^4\overline{A}}{d\sigma^4}=(k''+3kk'+k^3+4k\varepsilon)\,e_1+(4k'+7k^2+\varepsilon)\,\overline{e}_2;\\
&\frac{d^5\overline{A}}{d\sigma^5}=(k'''+4kk''+3k'^2+6k^2k'+8k'\varepsilon+k^4+11k^2\varepsilon+\\
&\qquad +13)\overline{e}_1+(5k''+25kk'+15k^3+6k\varepsilon)\overline{e}_2;\\
&\ldots\ldots\ldots\ldots\ldots\ldots\ldots\ldots\ldots\ldots
\end{aligned}\right\} \tag{7.3}$$

Assuming that the position of the point A on the line (A) is given by the value $\sigma=0$, we can write $d\sigma$ for σ. Then from equations (7.1–7.3) we obtain the equation for the line (A) in the canonical frame $(A, \overline{e}_1, \overline{e}_2)$:

$$\left.\begin{aligned}
x^1&=\sigma+\frac{k}{2}\sigma^2+\frac{k'+k^2+\varepsilon}{6}\sigma^3+\frac{k''+3kk'+k^3+4\varepsilon k}{24}\sigma^4+\\
&+\frac{k'''+4k''+3k'^2+6k^2k'+8\varepsilon k'+k^4+11k^2\varepsilon+\varepsilon^2}{120}\sigma^5+\ldots,\\
x^2&=\frac{1}{2}\sigma^2+\frac{k}{2}\sigma^3+\frac{4k'+7k^2+\varepsilon}{24}\sigma^4+\\
&+\frac{5k''+25kk'+15k^3+6\varepsilon k}{120}\sigma^5+\ldots
\end{aligned}\right\} \tag{7.4}$$

In the neighborhood of the point A, the line (A) differs very little from a parabola, the equations of which are

$$x^1=\sigma;\qquad x^2=\frac{1}{2}\sigma^2. \tag{7.5}$$

Several corollaries can be obtained from equations (7.4).

Corollary 1. In the neighborhood of the point A the arc a of the line (A) lies on one side of the tangent Ax^1. The unit point E_2 lines on the Ax^2 axis in the indicated half-plane.

Corollary 2. If the arc a lies in the neighborhood of the point A, then there exists a straight line parallel to the tangent Ax^1 and intersecting this arc at two and only two points.

By the diameter of the plane arc a with vertex at the point A of this arc will be meant the line consisting of the midpoints of the chords of the arc a that are parallel to the tangent Ax^1.

§ 8. Evolute. By the evolute (affine) of a line is meant the envelope of its affine normals. If the point C is the characteristic point of the family of normals of the line (A) on the normal at the point A, then the radius vector $\overline{C}$ of this point can be expressed in the form

$$\overline{C}=\overline{A}+\lambda\overline{e}_2 \tag{8.1}$$

under the condition of collinearity of the vectors $\overline{e}_2$ and $\frac{d\overline{C}}{d\sigma}$. Differentiation of equation (8.1) with respect to σ and use of formulas (6.1) and the indicated condition gives

$$\overline{C}=\overline{A}-\frac{1}{\varepsilon}\overline{e}_2. \tag{8.2}$$

The characteristic point of the family of normals of the line (A) on the normal at the point A will be called the center of curvature of the line (A) corresponding to the point A.

If the point A is of the hyperbolic type ($\varepsilon=1$), then the center of curvature C and the arc of the line in the neighborhood of the point A lie in different half-planes with respect to the tangent Ax^1, $\overline{AC}=-\overline{e}_2$ and the points C and E_2

are symmetrically situated with respect to the point A; if the point A is of the elliptic type ($\varepsilon = -1$), then $\overline{AC} = \overline{e}_2$ and the unit point E_2 of the Ax^2 axis coincides with the center of curvature C; for a point of the parabolic type ($\varepsilon = 0$), there is no corresponding center of curvature.

§ 9. Lines of zero curvature. Setting the curvature k equal to zero in equations (6.1), calculating the derivative $\frac{d^3\overline{A}}{d\sigma^3}$ and eliminating $\overline{e}_1$ and $\overline{e}_2$, we obtain the differential equation

$$\frac{d^3\overline{A}}{d\sigma^3} - \varepsilon \frac{d\overline{A}}{d\sigma} = 0. \tag{9.1}$$

The corresponding characteristic equation is:

$$h^3 - \varepsilon h = 0. \tag{9.2}$$

Integration of the differential equation (9.1) depends on the type of the point A.

1. Point A is of the hyperbolic type, $\varepsilon = 1$.

The roots of the characteristic equation (9.2) are:

$$h_0 = 0; \quad h_1 = 1; \quad h_2 = -1.$$

The general solution of equation (9.1) is

$$\overline{A}(\sigma) = \overline{c}_0 + \overline{c}_1 e^{\sigma} + \overline{c}_2 e^{-\sigma}, \tag{9.3}$$

which is the equation of a hyperbola.

2. Point A is of the elliptic type, $\varepsilon = -1$.

The roots of the characteristic equation (9.2) are:

$$h_0 = 0; \quad h_1 = i; \quad h_2 = -i.$$

The general solution of equation (9.1) is

$$\overline{A}(\sigma) = \overline{c}_0 + \overline{c}_1 \cos\sigma + \overline{c}_2 \sin\sigma, \tag{9.4}$$

which is the equation of an ellipse.

3. Point A is of the parabolic type, $\varepsilon = 0$.

All three roots of the characteristic equation (9.2) are zero. The general solution of equation (9.1) is

$$\overline{A}(\sigma) = \overline{c}_0 + \overline{c}_1\sigma + \overline{c}_2 \frac{\sigma^2}{2}, \tag{9.5}$$

which is the equation of a parabola.

§ 10. Osculating line of second order (quadric). Let us consider the relation of the line (A) to the line of zero curvature in the general canonical frame $(A, \overline{e}_1, \overline{e}_2)$ under the condition that the point A be of the same type for both curves.

1. Point A is of the hyperbolic type. From equations (9.3) and (6.1) we obtain

$$\overline{A} = \overline{c}_0 + \overline{c}_1 + \overline{c}_2 = 0;$$

$$\left.\frac{d\overline{A}}{d\sigma}\right|_{\sigma=0} = \overline{c}_1 - \overline{c}_2 = \overline{e}_1;$$

$$\left.\frac{d^2\overline{A}}{d\sigma^2}\right|_{\sigma=0} = \overline{c}_1 + \overline{c}_2 = \overline{e}_2.$$

Solving these equations for $\bar{c}_0, \bar{c}_1, \bar{c}_2$ we obtain

$$\bar{c}_0 = -\bar{e}_2; \quad \bar{c}_1 = \frac{\bar{e}_1 + \bar{e}_2}{2}; \quad \bar{c}_2 = \frac{\bar{e}_2 - \bar{e}_1}{2}.$$

Introducing these expressions into equation (9.3), we obtain

$$\bar{A}(\sigma) = (sh\sigma)\,\bar{e}_1 + (ch\sigma - 1)\,\bar{e}_2. \tag{10.1}$$

The equations of this line in parametric form are

$$x^1 = sh\sigma; \quad x^2 = ch\sigma - 1. \tag{10.2}$$

Eliminating the parameter σ, we obtain the equation in implicit form

$$(x^2 + 1)^2 - x^{1^2} = 1. \tag{10.3}$$

This hyperbola osculates with the line (A) at the point A. Its center coincides with the center of curvature of the line (A) for the point A. The unit point on the affine normal of the canonical frame $(A, \bar{e}_1, \bar{e}_2)$ is symmetric to the center of curvature with respect to the origin of the frame. The asymptotes of the hyperbola intersect the axis Ax^1 at two points the radius vectors of which are $\bar{A}+\bar{e}_1$ and $\bar{A}-\bar{e}_1$. The coordinate axes are conjugate with reference to the hyperbola.

2. Point A is of the elliptic type. From equations (9.4) and (6.1) we obtain

$$\bar{A} = \bar{c}_0 + \bar{c}_1 = 0;$$

$$\left.\frac{d\bar{A}}{d\sigma}\right|_{\sigma=0} = \bar{c}_2 = \bar{e}_1;$$

$$\left.\frac{d^2\bar{A}}{d\sigma^2}\right|_{\sigma=0} = -\bar{c}_1 = \bar{e}_2.$$

Introducing the expressions which we have obtained for $\bar{c}_0, \bar{c}_1, \bar{c}_2$ into equation (9.4), we obtain

$$\bar{A}(\sigma) = (\sin\sigma)\,\bar{e}_1 + (1 - \cos\sigma)\,\bar{e}_2. \tag{10.4}$$

In parametric form the equations of this line are

$$x^1 = \sin\sigma; \quad x^2 = 1 - \cos\sigma; \tag{10.5}$$

in implicit form the equation is

$$x^{1^2} + (x^2 - 1)^2 = 1. \tag{10.6}$$

This ellipse osculates with the line (A) at the point A. Its center coincides with the center of curvature of the line (A) for the point A and with the unit point of the canonical frame on the affine normal. The coordinate axes are conjugate with reference to the ellipse. One of the tangents to the ellipse that are parallel to the Ax^2 axis – affine normal, intersects the Ax^1 axis at the unit point on this axis, while the other intersects this axis at a point symmetric to the latter point with reference to the origin A.

3. Point A is of the parabolic type. From equations (9.5) and (6.1),

$$\bar{A} = \bar{c}_0 = 0;$$

$$\left.\frac{d\bar{A}}{d\sigma}\right|_{\sigma=0} = \bar{c}_1 = \bar{e}_1;$$

$$\left.\frac{d^2\bar{A}}{d\sigma^2}\right|_{\sigma=0} = \bar{e}_2.$$

Therefore equation (9.5) assumes the form

$$\bar{A}(\sigma) = \sigma\bar{e}_1 + \frac{\sigma^2}{2}\bar{e}_2. \tag{10.7}$$

In parametric form the equations for this line are

$$x^1 = \sigma; \quad x^2 = \frac{\sigma^2}{2}. \tag{10.8}$$

In implicit form

$$x^{1^2} = 2x^2. \tag{10.9}$$

This parabola osculates with the line (A) at the point A. The Ax^2 axis is the diameter of the parabola conjugate with the Ax^1 axis.

§ 11. Exercises. 1. The center of curvature of the line (A) corresponding to the point A of the hyperbolic type lies on the affine normal on the convex side of the line (A) in the neighborhood of the point A.

2. The center of curvature of the line (A) corresponding to the point A of the elliptical type lies on the affine normal on the concave side of the line (A) in the neighborhood of the point A.

3. At a point of the parabolic type a line has no center of curvature.

4. Theorem. If the line (A) has a point A of the hyperbolic or elliptic type and a line (Q) of second order has three consecutive points in common with (A) at the point A, while at the point B, symmetric to A with respect to the center of curvature of the line (A) for the point A, the tangent to the line (Q) is parallel to the tangent to the line (A) at the point A, then the canonical frames of these lines are indentical. (Line (Q) has a constant zero curvature.)

The frame of reference is determined by the Frenet-Cartan formulas (6.1).

5. Theorem. A line occupying the limiting position of a line of the second order passing through a point A of the parabolic type on the line (A) and through four points infinitely close to the latter point on this line, is an osculating parabola (10.9).

Chapter II

RELATION BETWEEN THE CANONICAL FRAME AND THE LINE

§ 1. Affine normal. We consider the line (A), specified by equations (7.4) of Chapter I in the canonical frame $(A, \bar{e}_1, \bar{e}_2)$.

Let $A(\sigma)$ and $A(\sigma_1)$ be points of this line lying in the neighborhood of the point A on a straight line parallel to the Ox^1 axis.

The coordinates x^i and x_1^i of these points are, respectively:

$$\left.\begin{aligned} x^1 &= \sigma + \frac{k}{2}\sigma^2 + \dots, \\ x^2 &= \frac{1}{2}\sigma^2 + \frac{k}{2}\sigma^3 + \dots, \end{aligned}\right\} \tag{1.1}$$

$$\left.\begin{aligned} x_1^1 &= \sigma_1 + \frac{k}{2}\sigma_1^2 + \ldots, \\ x_1^2 &= \frac{1}{2}\sigma_1^2 + \frac{k}{2}\sigma_1^3 + \ldots, \end{aligned}\right\} \tag{1.2}$$

and

$$\frac{1}{2}\sigma^2 + \frac{k}{2}\sigma^3 + \ldots = \frac{1}{2}\sigma_1^2 + \frac{k}{2}\sigma_1^3 + \ldots, \tag{1.3}$$

or, when $\sigma \neq \sigma_1$,

$$\sigma + \sigma_1 = -\frac{k}{2}\left(\sigma^2 + \sigma_1^2\right) + \ldots, \tag{1.4}$$

$$\lim \frac{\sigma}{\sigma_1} = -1. \tag{1.5}$$

The coordinates ξ^1, ξ^2 of the midpoint M of the segment $A(\sigma)A(\sigma_1)$ are:

$$\xi^1 = \frac{x^1 + x_1^1}{2} = \frac{\sigma + \sigma_1}{2} + \frac{k}{4}\left(\sigma^2 + \sigma_1^2\right) + \ldots;\ \xi^2 = \frac{1}{4}\sigma^2 + \frac{k}{4}\sigma^3 + \ldots$$

Consequently, using (1.4),

$$\lim_{\sigma \to 0} (\xi^1 : \xi^2) = 0. \tag{1.6}$$

This means that the affine normal to the line (A) at the point A is the tangent to the diameter of this line at the vertex A (§ 7, Chapter I).

§ 2. Position of the canonical frame relative to the line and a point of the hyperbolic or elliptic type on it. The position of the Ax^1 and Ax^2 axes of the canonical frame $(A, \overline{e_1}, \overline{e_2})$ relative to the line (A) and the point A of the hyperbolic or elliptic type on it is known (§ 1).

The vector $\overline{e_2}$ is symmetric to the vector $\overline{AC}$ if C is the center of curvature and the point A is of the hyperbolic type, and the vector $\overline{AC} = \overline{e_2}$ if the point A is of the elliptic type (§ 8, Chapter I). It remains to determine the relation between the line (A) and the vector $\overline{e_1}$. If the point A is of the hyperbolic type, then the unit point E_1 of the $\overline{Ax^1}$ axis lies at the intersection of the Ax^1 axis and the asymptote of the osculating quadric (§ 10, Chapter I); however, if the point A is of the elliptic type then one of the tangents to the osculating ellipse parallel to the Ax^2 axis intersects the Ax^1 axis at the unit point E_1 of the Ax^1 axis.

§ 3. Position of the canonical frame relative to the line and a point of the parabolic type on it. The positions of the Ax^1 and Ax^2 axes of the canonical frame $(A, \overline{e_1}, \overline{e_2})$ relative to the line (A) and the point A of the parabolic type on it are known (§ 1, Chapter II and § 10, Chapter I). The unit point E_1 of the Ax^1 axis can be chosen arbitrarily, excluding the point A (§4, Chapter I).

Let the straight line passing through the point E_1 parallel to the Ax^2 axis intersect the osculating parabola (10.9, Chapter I) at the point M, and let the point N on the straight line E_1M be symmetric to the point E_1 with respect to the point M. The straight line passing through the point N parallel to the Ax^1 axis intersects the Ax^2 axis at the point E_2, the unit point on the Ax^2 axis.

§ 4. Geometric interpretation of curvature. Let the point B be symmetric to the center of curvature C corresponding to the point A with respect to A. The radius vector of B in any coordinate system may be written, with the aid of equations (8.2, Chapter 10) in the form

$$\overline{B} = \overline{A} + \frac{1}{\varepsilon}\overline{e}_2. \tag{4.1}$$

If the point A describes a line (A), then point B, generally speaking, describes some line (B). The vector of the tangent to this line at B is obtained by differentiating both sides of equation (4.1) and making use of formulas (6.1, Chapter I):

$$\frac{d\overline{B}}{d\sigma} = 2\left(\overline{e}_1 + \frac{k}{\varepsilon}\overline{e}_2\right). \tag{4.2}$$

The equation of the tangent to the line (B) at the point B is

$$\overline{X} = \overline{B} + \rho\frac{d\overline{B}}{d\sigma}. \tag{4.3}$$

This equation can be written in the frame $(A, \overline{e}_1, \overline{e}_2)$ with the aid of equations (4.1–4.2) in the following form:

$$\overline{AX} = 2\rho\overline{e}_1 + \frac{1}{\varepsilon}(1+2k\rho)\,\overline{e}_2. \tag{4.4}$$

The point D at the intersection of the straight line (4.4) and the Ax^1 axis is obtained from the condition

$$1 + 2k\rho = 0. \tag{4.5}$$

The coordinates of D are $\left(-\frac{1}{k}, 0\right)$. We have obtained the geometric interpretation of the curvature k.

The tangent to the line (B) at the point B, which corresponds to the point A and the center of curvature C, intersects the Ax^1 axis of the canonical frame referred to the line (A) and the point A at the point $D\left(-\frac{1}{k}, O\right)$, the first coordinate of which is the inverse, in magnitude and sign, of the curvature of the line (A) corresponding to the point A.

Let us give another geometric interpretation of affine curvature. If we draw a straight line through D parallel to the straight line E_1E_2 to its intersection with the Ax^2 axis at the point H, and another straight line through E_2 parallel to the straight line E_1H to its intersection with the Ax^1 axis at the point K, then the coordinates of K will be $(-k, o)$.

§ 5. **Exercises. 1.** Find the lines with constant affine curvature.

Answer. From the system of equations (6.1) of Chapter I, for constant curvature k we obtain a differential equation of the third order with constant coefficients

$$\frac{d^3\overline{A}}{d\sigma^3} - 3k\frac{d^2\overline{A}}{d\sigma^2} + (2k^2 - \varepsilon)\frac{d\overline{A}}{d\sigma} = 0.$$

Integrating it we can obtain the required equations in the form

$$x^2 = x^{1\frac{3k - \sqrt{k^2+4}}{3k + \sqrt{k^2+4}}} \qquad \left(\varepsilon = 1,\ \ k^2 \neq \frac{1}{2}\right);$$

$$x^2 = e^{x^1} \qquad \left(\varepsilon = 1,\ \ k^2 = \frac{1}{2}\right);$$

$$x^2 = x^{1\frac{3k - \sqrt{k^2 - 4}}{3k + \sqrt{k^2 - 4}}} \qquad (\varepsilon = -1, \quad k^2 > 4);$$

$$x^1 = e^{\frac{x^2}{x^1}} \qquad (\varepsilon = -1, \quad k^2 = 4);$$

$$\sqrt{x^{1^2} + x^{2^2}} \cos \left[\frac{\sqrt{4 - k^2}}{6k} \ln \left(x^{1^2} + x^{2^2}\right)\right] = x^1$$

$$(\varepsilon = -1, \; 0 < k^2 < 4);$$

$$x^{1^2} + x^{2^2} = 1 \qquad (\varepsilon = -1, \quad k = 0);$$

$$x^{1^2} - x^{2^2} = 1 \qquad (\varepsilon = 1, \quad k = 0);$$

$$x^{2^2} = 2x^1 \qquad (\varepsilon = 0).$$

2. Find the lines for which all affine normals form a pencil.

Answer. The only such lines are those of zero curvature. If the pencil of normals has a center, then the line with these normals is an ellipse ($\varepsilon = -1$) or a hyperbola ($\varepsilon = 1$); but if the normals form a pencil of parallel straight lines, then the line is a parabola.

Part Two
LINES IN SPACE

Chapter III

THE CANONICAL FRAME

§ 1. Fundamental relations. The equation of a line (A) in three-dimensional affine space in the frame $(O, \bar{u}_1, \bar{u}_2, \bar{u}_3)$ with origin O and coordinate vectors $\bar{u}_1, \bar{u}_2, \bar{u}_3$ can be written as

$$\overline{OA} = x^i(t)\, u_i \quad (i, j, k = 1, 2, 3), \tag{1.1}$$

where $\overline{OA}$ is the radius vector of the generic point A of this line, t the parameter and $x^i\,(t)$ the coordinates of A. The equations for infinitesimal displacements of the frame $(A, \bar{e}_1, \bar{e}_2, \bar{e}_3)$ are:

$$d\bar{A} = \omega^i \bar{e}_i; \quad d\bar{e}_i = \omega_i^j \bar{e}_j. \tag{1.2}$$

The equations of structure corresponding to this system are:

$$D\omega^i = \left[\omega^j\, \omega_j^i\right]; \quad D\omega_i^j = \left[\omega_i^k\, \omega_k^j\right]. \tag{1.3}$$

§ 2. Frames of the first order. Let the point A describe the line (A), and let the frame $(A, \bar{e}_1, \bar{e}_2, \bar{e}_3)$ describe an affine motion such that the vector $\bar{e}_1$ remains collinear with $d\bar{A}$, i.e., the vector of the tangent to the line (A) at the point A. Then the first equation of the system (1.2) will be

$$d\bar{A} = \omega^1 \bar{e}_1; \tag{2.1}$$

$$\omega^\alpha = 0 \quad (\alpha = 2, 3). \tag{2.2}$$

The group of affine transformations of points in three-dimensional space depends on twelve parameters. In agreement with any such set of parameters, a second set may be constructed which will include the parameter t appearing in equation (1.1).

The equivalence of these sets resides in that to fixed values of all parameters of the first set there correspond fixed values of all parameters of the second set, and vice versa. The parameter t is called the principal form and the rest secondary forms.

The infinitesimal displacements of the frame $(A, \bar{e}_1, \bar{e}_2, \bar{e}_3)$ for fixed principal parameter depend on nine parameters which may be of the form

$$\omega_i^j\,(\delta) = \omega_i^j \Big|\, dt = 0. \tag{2.3}$$

The values of these parameters correspond to the transformations of the stationary subgroup which constitutes the centroaffine group with center at the point *A*. Consequently, to choose a canonical frame referred to the line *(A)* and the point *A*, it is necessary to continue equations (2.2) until one obtains nine relations which will permit referring the forms ω_i^j to a ring with a basis consisting of a single principal form ω^1.

§ 3. Continuation of equations (2.2). Continuing equations (2.2), we obtain

$$\left.\begin{aligned}
\omega_1^\alpha &= a_{11}^\alpha \omega^1;\\
da_{11}^\alpha &= 2a_{11}^\alpha \omega_1^1 - a_{11}^\beta \omega_\beta^\alpha + a_{21}^\alpha \omega^1;\\
da_{21}^\alpha &= 3a_{21}^\alpha \omega_1^1 + 3a_{11}^\alpha a_{11}^\beta \omega_\beta^1 - a_{21}^\beta \omega_\beta^\alpha + a_{31}^\alpha \omega^1;\\
da_{31}^\alpha &\quad 4a_{31}^\alpha \omega_1^1 + 6a_{21}^\alpha a_{11}^\beta \omega_\beta^1 + 4a_{11}^\alpha a_{21}^\beta \omega_\beta^1 - a_{31}^\beta \omega_\beta^\alpha + a_{41}^\alpha \omega^1;\\
da_{41}^\alpha &= 5a_{41}^\alpha \omega_1^1 + 10a_{31}^\alpha a_{11}^\beta \omega_\beta^1 + 10a_{21}^\alpha a_{21}^\beta \omega_\beta^1 + 5a_{11}^\alpha a_{31}^\beta \omega_\beta^1 -\\
&\qquad - a_{41}^\beta \omega_\beta^\alpha + a_{51}^\alpha \omega^1.
\end{aligned}\right\} \tag{3.1}$$

§ 4. Choice of a canonical frame. Let us set

$$a_{11}^2 = 1;\ a_{11}^3 = 0;\ a_{21}^2 = 0;\ a_{21}^3 = 1;\ a_{31}^2 = 0;\ a_{31}^3 = 0; \tag{4.1}$$

$$a_{41}^3 = -6\varepsilon, \tag{4.2}$$

where

$$\varepsilon = 1 \tag{4.3}$$

or

$$\varepsilon = -1. \tag{4.4}$$

From the system of equations (3.1) we obtain

$$\left.\begin{aligned}
&\omega_1^1 = k_1\omega^1;\ \omega_1^2 = \omega^1;\quad \omega_1^3 = 0;\\
&\omega_2^1 = \varepsilon\omega^1;\ \omega_2^2 = 2k_1\omega^1;\ \omega_2^3 = \omega^1;\\
&\omega_3^1 = k_2\omega^1;\ \omega_3^2 = 3\varepsilon\omega^1;\ \omega_3^3 = 3k_1\omega^1,
\end{aligned}\right\} \tag{4.5}$$

where

$$k_1 = \frac{1}{12\varepsilon}\left(a_{51}^3 - \frac{7}{2}a_{41}^2\right);\ k_2 = -\frac{a_{41}^2}{4}. \tag{4.6}$$

The point *A* will be said to be of the hyperbolic type if $\varepsilon = 1$ and of the elliptic type if $\varepsilon = -1$.

If the point *A* corresponds to the value

$$a_{41}^3 = 0, \tag{4.7}$$

then, from the conditions (1.2, Chapter III), (4.2), (4.5–4.6) it follows that

$$\left.\begin{aligned}
d\bar{e}_1 &= \omega_1^1\bar{e}_2 + \omega^1\bar{e}_3;\\
d\bar{e}_2 &= 2\omega_1^1\bar{e}_2 + \omega^1\bar{e}_3;\\
d\bar{e}_3 &= -\frac{a_{41}^2}{4}\omega^1\bar{e}_1 + 3\omega_1^1\bar{e}_3.
\end{aligned}\right\} \tag{4.8}$$

We set

$$\delta\bar{e}_i = d\bar{e}_i\Big|_{\omega^1} = 0;\ \omega_i^j(\delta) = \omega_i^j\Big|_{\omega_1} = 0.$$

If

$$\omega^1 = 0,$$

then we obtain, from the system of equations (4.8), the equations for infinitesimal displacements of the frame $(A, \overline{e}_1, \overline{e}_2, \overline{e}_3)$ with fixed point A in the form

$$\delta\overline{e}_1 = \omega_1^1(\delta)\,\overline{e}_1;$$
$$\delta\overline{e}_2 = 2\omega_1^1(\delta)\,\overline{e}_2;$$
$$\delta\overline{e}_3 = 3\omega_1^1(\delta)\,\overline{e}_3.$$

This means that the coordinate axes of the frame of reference $(A, \overline{e}_1, \overline{e}_2, \overline{e}_3)$ have been chosen, but the coordinate vectors $\overline{e}_1, \overline{e}_2, \overline{e}_3$ constitute a one-parameter family. The point A will be said to be of the parabolic type if $\varepsilon = 0$. For this condition the first equation of the system (4.6) becomes meaningless. However, even for this point we will denote the form ω_1^1 by $k_1\omega^1$, remembering that here k_1 is not the quantity defined by formula (4.6 : 1). Now the equations for infinitesimal displacements of the canonical frame referred to a line and a point of the hyperbolic or elliptic type can be combined formally with the corresponding equations for infinitesimal displacements of a frame referred to a point of the parabolic type, and can be written in the form

$$\left.\begin{aligned} d\overline{A} &= \omega^1\overline{e}_1;\\ d\overline{e}_1 &= k_1\omega^1\overline{e}_1 + \omega^1\overline{e}_2;\\ d\overline{e}_2 &= \varepsilon\omega^1\overline{e}_1 + 2k_1\omega^1\overline{e}_2 + \omega^1\overline{e}_3;\\ d\overline{e}_3 &= k_2\omega^1\overline{e}_1 + 3\varepsilon\omega^1\overline{e}_2 + 3k_1\omega^1\overline{e}_3. \end{aligned}\right\} \tag{4.9}$$

§ 5. Natural parameter. Frenet-Cartan formulas. The exterior differential of the principal form is

$$D\omega^1 = \left[\omega^i\omega_i^1\right] = \left[\omega^1\omega_1^1\right] = \left[\omega^1 k_1\omega^1\right] = 0.$$

Therefore one can set

$$\omega^1 = d\sigma. \tag{5.1}$$

The parameter σ will be termed natural. Formulas (4.9) can now be written in the form

$$\left.\begin{aligned} \frac{d\overline{A}}{d\sigma} &= \overline{e}_1;\\ \frac{d\overline{e}_1}{d\sigma} &= k_1\overline{e}_1 + \overline{e}_2;\\ \frac{d\overline{e}_2}{d\sigma} &= \varepsilon\overline{e}_1 + 2k_1\overline{e}_2 + \overline{e}_3;\\ \frac{d\overline{e}_3}{d\sigma} &= k_2\overline{e}_1 + 3\varepsilon\overline{e}_2 + 3k_1\overline{e}_3. \end{aligned}\right\} \tag{5.2}$$

In these Frenet-Cartan formulas, which correspond to the line (A), the functions

$$k_1 = k_1(\sigma);\ k_2 = k_2(\sigma) \tag{5.3}$$

will be called respectively the first and second curvature of the line (A) at the point $A(\sigma)$.

§ 6. Equations of a line in its canonical frame. By differentiation we obtain from formulas (5.2)

$$\left.\begin{aligned}
&\frac{d\bar{A}}{d\sigma} = \bar{e}_1;\\
&\frac{d^2\bar{A}}{d\sigma^2} = k_1\bar{e}_1 + \bar{e}_2;\\
&\frac{d^3\bar{A}}{d\sigma^3} = \left(k_1' + k_1^2 + \varepsilon\right)\bar{e}_1 + 3k_1\bar{e}_2 + \bar{e}_3;\\
&\frac{d^4\bar{A}}{d\sigma^4} = \left(k_1'' + 3k_1k_1' + k_1^3 + 4k_1\varepsilon + k_2\right)\bar{e}_1 + \left(4k_1' +\right.\\
&\qquad\qquad \left. + 7k_1^2 + 4\varepsilon\right)\bar{e}_2 + 6k_1\bar{e}_3;\\
&\frac{d^5\bar{A}}{d\sigma^5} = a\bar{e}_1 + b\bar{e}_2 + \left(10k_1' + 25k_1^2 + 4\varepsilon\right)\bar{e}_3;\\
&\ldots\ldots\ldots\ldots\ldots\ldots\ldots\ldots\ldots\ldots
\end{aligned}\right\} \qquad (6.1)$$

The primes denote derivatives in σ and the coefficients a and b certain functions of k_1, k_2 and their derivatives. The fixed point A of line (A) may be regarded as corresponding to the value $\sigma = 0$ after changing, if necessary, all values of σ by the same amount. If the vector function $A\ (\sigma)$ is expanded in a Maclaurin series in the neighborhood of the point $A(0)=A$,

$$\bar{A}\,(\sigma) = \bar{A} + \frac{\sigma}{1!}\frac{d\bar{A}}{d\sigma} + \frac{\sigma^2}{2!}\frac{d^2\bar{A}}{d\sigma^2} + \frac{\sigma^3}{3!}\frac{d^3\bar{A}}{d\sigma^3} + \frac{\sigma^4}{4!}\frac{d^4\bar{A}}{d\sigma^4} + \frac{\sigma^5}{5!}\frac{d^5\bar{A}}{d\sigma^5} + \ldots,$$

then, with the aid of formulas (6.1), this expansion may be written in the form

$$\begin{aligned}
\bar{A}\,(\sigma) &= \sigma\bar{e}_1 + \frac{\sigma^2}{2}(k_1\bar{e}_1 + \bar{e}_2) + \frac{\sigma^3}{6}\left[\left(k_1' + k_1^2 + \varepsilon\right)\bar{e}_1 + 3k_1\bar{e}_2 + \bar{e}_3\right] +\\
&+ \frac{\sigma^4}{24}\left[\left(k_1'' + 3k_1k_1' + k_1^3 + 4k_1\varepsilon + k_2\right)\bar{e}_1 + \left(4k_1' + 7k_1^2 + 4\varepsilon\right)\bar{e}_2 +\right.\\
&\left.+ 6k_1\bar{e}_3\right] + \frac{\sigma^5}{120}\left[a\bar{e}_1 + b\bar{e}_2 + \left(10k_1' + 25k_1^2 + 4\varepsilon\right)\bar{e}_3\right] + \ldots
\end{aligned} \qquad (6.2)$$

If x^1, x^2, x^3 are the coordinates of the point $A\ (\sigma)$ in the frame $(A, \bar{e}_1, \bar{e}_2, \bar{e}_3)$, then the equations of the line (A) in its canonical frame can be written in the form

$$\left.\begin{aligned}
x^1 &= \sigma + \frac{k_1}{2}\sigma^2 + \frac{k_1' + k_1^2 + \varepsilon}{6}\sigma^3 + \frac{k_1'' + 3k_1k_1' + k_1^3 + 4\varepsilon k_1 + k_2}{24}\sigma^4 + \ldots,\\
x^2 &= \frac{1}{2}\sigma^2 + \frac{k_1}{2}\sigma^3 + \frac{4k_1' + 7k_1^2 + 4\varepsilon}{24}\sigma^4 + \ldots,\\
x^3 &= \frac{1}{6}\sigma^3 + \frac{k_1}{4}\sigma^4 + \frac{10k_1' + 25k_1^2 + 4\varepsilon}{120}\sigma^5 + \ldots
\end{aligned}\right\} \qquad (6.3)$$

§ 7. Osculating line of the third order. The form of the arc of the line (A) in the neighborhood of the point A and its position in the canonical frame can be judged by comparing this arc with the arc of the line given by the equations

$$x^1 = \sigma;\ x^2 = \frac{1}{2}\sigma^2;\ x^3 = \frac{1}{6}\sigma^3. \qquad (7.1)$$

Here the right-hand sides contain only the first terms of the expansion (6.3).

The line (7.1) represents the common part of a cylinder

$$x^{1^2} - 2x^2 = 0, \qquad (7.2)$$

and a cone

$$2x^{2^2} - 3x^1x^3 = 0, \tag{7.3}$$

apart from the Ax^3 axis. This line is of the third order and osculates with the line (A) at the point A.

Chapter IV

RELATION BETWEEN THE CANONICAL FRAME AND THE LINE

§ 1. Osculating plane. The equation of the plane osculating with the line (A) at the point A can be written in the form

$$\left|\overline{X} - \overline{A},\ \frac{d\overline{A}}{d\sigma},\ \frac{d^2\overline{A}}{d\sigma^2}\right| = 0. \tag{1.1}$$

The symbol in the left-hand side of the equation denotes the determinant the columns of which consist of the coordinate vectors $\overline{X} - \overline{A}, \frac{d\overline{A}}{d\sigma}, \frac{d^2\overline{A}}{d\sigma^2}$, $\overline{X}$ being the radius vector of the generic point of the plane.

In the frame $(A, \overline{e}_1, \overline{e}_2, \overline{e}_3)$ the equation (1.1) can, with the help of formulas (5.2) of Chapter III, be written in the form

$$|\overline{X}, \overline{e}_1, \overline{e}_2| = 0.$$

This means that the plane containing the Ax^1 and Ax^2 axes of the canonical frame $(A, \overline{e}_1, \overline{e}_2, \overline{e}_3)$ is the osculating plane to the line (A) at the point A.

We will call the Ax^2 axis the principal normal, the Ax^3 axis the binormal, the plane x^2Ax^3 the normal plane, and the plane x^3Ax^4 the rectifying plane of the line (A) at the point A.

Several corollaries can be obtained from equations (6.3) of Chapter III.

Corollary 1. If the arc of the line (A) lies in the neighborhood of the point A, then there exists a plane parallel to the osculating plane x^1Ax^2 which intersects this arc at a single point.

Corollary 2. The point A divides the arc of the line (A) in the neighborhood into two parts lying in different regions of space separated by the osculating plane x^1Ax^2.

Corollary 3. Through a point on the arc of the line (A) in the neighborhood of A there passes only one chord of this arc with its midpoint in the osculating plane x^1Ax^2.

Indeed, let the point A (σ) be sufficiently close to A (sufficiently small absolute value of σ) and B be an arbitrary point on the plane x^1Ax^2.

Through the point C, symmetric to the point A (σ) with respect to B, there passes a plane parallel to the plane x^1Ax^2 and intersecting the arc of the line (A) at a single point A (σ_1) (Corollary 1).

§ 2. Principal normal. In the neighborhood of the point A the arc a, situated in three-dimensional space and having only one point C in common with the plane osculating with it, is related by affine properties to another line which we will call the diameter.

Its definition is as follows.

By the diameter of the arc a with vertex at the point A on it we will mean the line consisting of the point A and the midpoints of the chords of the arc a that lie in the osculating plane of the arc a at the point A. Let us prove the following assertion, which contains a geometric interpretation of the principal normal.

The principal normal of the line (A) at the point A is the tangent to the diameter of this line at the vertex A.

Let the points $P_1(x_1^i)$ and $P_2(x_2^i)$ on the line (A), corresponding to the values of the parameter $\sigma=\sigma_1$ and $\sigma=\sigma_2$, be the ends of the chord P_1P_2 of this line with midpoint $M(y^i)$, lying in the osculating plane to the line (A) at A. The coordinates (x_1^i) and (x_2^i) are related to the values of σ_1 and σ_2 by equations (6.3) of Chapter III.

$$\left.\begin{aligned} x_1^1 &= \sigma_1+\frac{k_1}{2}\sigma_1^2+\dots,\\ x_1^2 &= \frac{1}{2}\sigma_1^2+\frac{k_1}{2}\sigma_1^3+\dots,\\ x_1^3 &= \frac{1}{6}\sigma_1^3+\frac{k_1}{4}\sigma_1^4+\dots,\end{aligned}\right\} \tag{2.1}$$

$$\left.\begin{aligned} x_2^1 &= \sigma_2+\frac{k_1}{2}\sigma_2^2+\dots,\\ x_2^2 &= \frac{1}{2}\sigma_2^2+\frac{k_1}{2}\sigma_2^3+\dots,\\ x_2^3 &= \frac{1}{6}\sigma_2^3+\frac{k_1}{4}\sigma_2^4+\dots,\end{aligned}\right\} \tag{2.2}$$

The conditions that the chord P_1P_2 with midpoint M lies in the plane x^1Ax^2 are:

$$x_1^3=-x_2^3; \tag{2.3}$$

$$\left.\begin{aligned} y^1 &= \frac{x_1^1+x_2^1}{2}=\frac{\sigma_1+\sigma_2}{2}+\frac{k_1}{4}\left(\sigma_1^2+\sigma_2^2\right)+\dots,\\ y^2 &= \frac{x_1^2+x_2^2}{2}=\frac{1}{4}\left(\sigma_1^2+\sigma_2^2\right)+\frac{k_1}{4}\left(\sigma_1^3+\sigma_2^3\right)+\dots,\\ y^3 &= 0.\end{aligned}\right\} \tag{2.4}$$

It follows from equations (2.1–2.3) that:

$$\sigma_1+\sigma_2=-\frac{k_1}{2}\left(\sigma_1^2+\sigma_2^2\right)+\dots, \tag{2.5}$$

$$\lim_{\sigma_2\to 0}\frac{\sigma_1}{\sigma_2}=-1. \tag{2.6}$$

For $\sigma_2\to 0$ (or $\sigma_1\to 0$) the point $M\to A$ and the secant AM becomes tangent to the diameter (M) at its vertex A (if such a tangent exists).

From equations (2.4–2.5) we obtain

$$\frac{y^1}{y^2}=\frac{a\left(\sigma_1^3+\sigma_2^3\right)+\dots}{\frac{1}{2}\left(\sigma_1^2+\sigma_2^2\right)+\dots}. \tag{2.7}$$

The numerator in the right-hand side is an infinitesimal of at least the third order, the denominator of the second order; a is a certain coefficient.

If therefore follows from equations (2.6–2.7) that

$$\lim_{\sigma_2 \to 0} \frac{y^1}{y_2} = 0.$$

Now this means that the principal normal Ax^2 is tangent to the diameter *(M)* at the vertex *A*.

§ 3. Rectifying plane. The equations of a cylindrical surface with directrix (*A*) and generators parallel to the Ax^1 axis can be obtained with the aid of equations (6.3) of Chapter III in the form

$$\left.\begin{aligned} x^2 &= \frac{1}{2}\sigma^2 + \frac{k_1}{2}\sigma^3 + \dots, \\ x^3 &= \frac{1}{6}\sigma^3 + \frac{k_1}{4}\sigma^4 + \dots, \end{aligned}\right\}. \tag{3.1}$$

The equation of the tangent plane to this surface at the point (x^i) with generic coordinates y^i is

$$\frac{y^2 - x^2}{\frac{dx^2}{d\sigma}} = \frac{y^3 - x^3}{\frac{dx^3}{d\sigma}},$$

or

$$\frac{y^2 - \left(\frac{1}{2}\sigma^2 + \frac{k_1}{2}\sigma^3 + \dots\right)}{\sigma + \frac{3}{2}k_1\sigma^2 + \dots} = \frac{y^3 - \left(\frac{1}{6}\sigma^3 + \frac{k_1}{4}\sigma^4 + \dots\right)}{\frac{1}{2}\sigma^2 + k_1\sigma^3 + \dots}. \tag{3.2}$$

The intersection between this plane and the osculating plane x^1Ax^2 is the straight line for which the equations are

$$\left.\begin{aligned} y^2 &= \frac{1}{6}\sigma^2 + \frac{k_1}{6}\sigma^3 + \dots, \\ y^3 &= 0. \end{aligned}\right\} \tag{3.3}$$

The cylindrical surface (3.1) consists of two sheets osculating with the plane x^1Ax^2 along the straight line Ax^1. Let the generator of the surface (3.1) correspond to the value $\sigma = \sigma_1$; the plane (3.2) osculates with the surface along this straight line. For $\sigma = \sigma_1$ we obtain a definite straight line (3.3). If the number σ_1 is sufficiently small, then through the straight line (3.3) there passes a plane tangent to the other sheet of the surface (3.1) along the straight line corresponding to a certain value of $\sigma = \sigma_2$. The condition that the latter plane pass through the straight line (3.3) for $\sigma = \sigma_1$ is as follows:

$$\frac{\left(\frac{1}{\sigma}\sigma_1^2 + \frac{k_1}{6}\sigma_1^3 + \dots\right) - \left(\frac{1}{2}\sigma_2^2 + \frac{k_1}{2}\sigma_2^3 + \dots\right)}{\sigma_2 + \frac{3}{2}k_1\sigma_2^2 + \dots} =$$

$$= \frac{-\left(\frac{1}{6}\sigma_2^3 + \frac{k_1}{4}\sigma_2^4 + \dots\right)}{\frac{1}{2}\sigma_2^2 + k_1\sigma_2^3 + \dots}.$$

Taking into account that the signs of $y\sigma_1$ and σ_2 should be different, we obtain

$$\sigma_1 + \frac{k_1}{2}\sigma_1^2 + \dots = -\left(\sigma_2 + \frac{k_1}{2}\sigma_2^2 + \dots\right). \tag{3.4}$$

Now we shall prove an assertion which gives a constructive method of obtaining the rectifying plane.

If a and b are the generators of the cylindrical surface (3.1) lying on different sides of the osculating plane x^1Ax^2 to the line (A) at the point A, and the tangent planes α and β to the surface (3.1) along these generators intersect along the straight line p in the plane x^1Ax^2, then upon (parallel) displacement of the straight line p till it coincides with the tangent Ax^1 the plane passing through the straight lines a and b will assume the limiting position of the rectifying plane to the line (A) at the point A.

The equation of the plane passing through the straight lines

$$x^2 = \frac{1}{2}\sigma_1^2 + \frac{k_1}{2}\sigma_1^3 + \dots,$$
$$x^3 = \frac{1}{6}\sigma_1^3 + \frac{k_1}{4}\sigma_1^4 + \dots,$$

and

$$x^2 = \frac{1}{2}\sigma_2^2 + \frac{k_1}{2}\sigma_2^3 + \dots,$$
$$x^3 = \frac{1}{6}\sigma_2^3 + \frac{k_1}{4}\sigma_2^4 + \dots,$$

which satisfy the condition (3.4) is

$$\begin{vmatrix} y^2, & \frac{1}{2}\sigma_1^2 + \frac{k_1}{2}\sigma_1^3 + \dots, & \frac{1}{2}\sigma_2^2 + \frac{k_1}{2}\sigma_2^3 + \dots \\ y^3, & \frac{1}{6}\sigma_1^3 + \frac{k_1}{4}\sigma_1^4 + \dots, & \frac{1}{6}\sigma_2^3 + \frac{k_1}{4}\sigma_2^4 + \dots \\ 1 & 1 & 1 \end{vmatrix} = 0,$$

or

$$y^2\left[\frac{1}{6}\sigma_1^3 + \frac{k_1}{4}\sigma_1^4 + \dots - \left(\frac{1}{6}\sigma_2^3 + \frac{k_1}{4}\sigma_2^4 + \dots\right) - y^3(a\sigma_1^4 + \dots) + \right.$$
$$\left. + \left[\frac{1}{12}(\sigma_1^2\sigma_2^3 - \sigma_1^3\sigma_2^2) + \dots\right] = 0,\right.$$

where a is a certain coefficient.

After dividing both sides of this equation by σ_1^3 and passing to the limit $\sigma_1 \to 0$, we obtain the equation of the rectifying plane

$$y^2 = 0.$$

§ 4. Binormal. Normal plane. Let the line (R) be the projection of the line (A) on the rectifying plane parallel to the principal normal. Its equations in this plane are:

$$\left.\begin{aligned} x^1 &= \sigma + \frac{k_1}{2}\sigma^2 + \frac{k_1' + k_1^2 + \varepsilon}{6}\sigma^3 + \dots, \\ x^3 &= \frac{1}{6}\sigma^3 + \frac{k_1}{4}\sigma^4 + \frac{1}{120}(10k_1' + 25k_1^2 + 4\varepsilon)\sigma^5 + \dots \end{aligned}\right\} \tag{4.1}$$

The tangent to this line at the point $R\,(x^1, x^3)$ is given by the equations:

$$y^1 = x^1 + \rho\frac{dx^1}{d\sigma};\quad y^3 = x^3 + \rho\frac{dx^3}{d\sigma}. \tag{4.2}$$

To the point of intersection M of the tangent (4.2) and the Ax^1 axis there corresponds the value of the parameter $\rho = -x^3 : \frac{dx^3}{d\sigma}$. Marking off three segments equal to RM, from the point R to the tangent in the direction RM, we obtain the point Q, where

$$\overline{AQ} = \left[\left(x^1 \frac{dx^3}{d\sigma} - 3x^3 \frac{dx^1}{d\sigma}\right) : \frac{dx^3}{d\sigma}\right]\bar{e}_1 - 2x^3\bar{e}_3. \tag{4.3}$$

From equations (4.1) and (4.3)

$$\overline{AQ} = \left(-\frac{1}{5}\sigma^3 + \dots\right)\bar{e}_1 - \left(\frac{1}{3}\sigma^3 + \dots\right)\bar{e}_3. \tag{4.4}$$

The equation of the tangent to the line (Q) at the point A is therefore obtained from the equation of the secant AQ

$$x^1 : \left(\frac{1}{5}\sigma^3 + \dots\right) = x^3 : \left(\frac{1}{3}\sigma^3 + \dots\right),$$

for $\sigma \to 0$ in the form

$$5x^1 - 3x^3 = 0. \tag{4.5}$$

Let us now find the characteristic of the family of rectifying planes of the line (A) on the rectifying plane x^1Ax^3. Regarding the radius vector $\bar{A}$ and the vectors $\bar{e}_1, \bar{e}_2, \bar{e}_3$ as vector functions of the natural parameter σ, we obtain the one-parameter family of rectifying planes given by the equation

$$|\bar{X} - \bar{A},\ \bar{e}_1,\ \bar{e}_3| = 0. \tag{4.6}$$

Differentiating this equation with respect to σ and using formulas (6.1) of Chapter III, we obtain the equation

$$|\bar{X} - \bar{A},\ \bar{e}_2,\ \bar{e}_3| + 3\,|\bar{X} - \bar{A},\ \bar{e}_1,\ \bar{e}_2| = 0. \tag{4.7}$$

The equation of the plane (4.7) in the coordinates referred to the frame $(A, \bar{e}_1, \bar{e}_2, \bar{e}_3)$ is

$$x^1 + 3x^3 = 0. \tag{4.8}$$

Let M, N, L be respectively the points of intersection of the straight lines (4.5), Ax^3, (4.8) with any straight line in the rectifying plane parallel to the Ax^1 axis. Then

$$NM : NL = -5. \tag{4.9}$$

Knowing the construction of the straight lines (4.5), (4.8), and making use of the relation (4.9), we can also obtain the binormal Ax^3. We will then obtain the composition of the normal plane x^2Ax^3.

§ 5. Coordinate vectors. Let us denote by the letter P the projection of the point A of the line (A) onto the plane x^1Ax^2 in a direction parallel to the binormal Ax^3, and by (P) the line which is the projection of the line (A) on this plane. The equations of the line (P) in the frame $(A, \bar{e}_1, \bar{e}_2)$ can be written down using equations (6.3) of Chapter III in parametric form:

$$\begin{aligned} x^1 &= \sigma + \frac{k_1}{2}\sigma^2 + \frac{k_1' + k_1^2 + \varepsilon}{6}\sigma^3 + \dots, \\ x^2 &= \frac{1}{2}\sigma^2 + \frac{k_1}{2}\sigma^3 + \frac{4k_1' + 7k_1^2 + 4\varepsilon}{24}\sigma^4 + \dots, \end{aligned} \tag{5.1}$$

or in vector form

$$\overline{AP}=\left(\sigma+\frac{k_1}{2}\sigma^2+\frac{k_1'+k_1^2+\varepsilon}{6}\sigma^3+\ldots\right)\overline{e}_1+\left(\frac{1}{2}\sigma^2+\frac{k_1}{2}\sigma^3+\right.$$
$$\left.+\frac{4k_1'+7k_1^2+4\varepsilon}{24}\sigma^4+\ldots\right)\overline{e}_2. \tag{5.2}$$

We will prove a proposition containing a geometric interpretation of the relationship of the vectors $\overline{e}_1, \overline{e}_2$ to the line (A) and its point A.

If $(A, \overline{e}_1, \overline{e}_2, \overline{e}_3)$ is the canonical frame referred to the line (A) and the point A, given by the Frenet-Cartan formulas (6.1) of Chapter III, and the line (P) is the projection of the line (A) onto the plane x^1Ax^2 along the direction $\overline{e}_3$, then $(A, \overline{e}_1, \overline{e}_2)$ is the canonical frame referred to the line (P) and its point A which is given by the Frenet-Cartan formulas (6.1) of Chapter I.

Indeed, calculating the derivatives $\frac{d\overline{P}}{d\sigma}, \frac{d^2\overline{P}}{d\sigma^2}, \frac{d^3\overline{P}}{d\sigma^3}$ of the vector function $\overline{AP}=\overline{P}$ defined by equation (5.2) and subsequently setting $\sigma=0$, we obtain

$$\frac{d\overline{P}}{d\sigma}\overline{e}_1;\ \frac{d\overline{e}_1}{d\sigma}=k_1\overline{e}_1+\overline{e}_2;\ \frac{d\overline{e}_2}{d\sigma}=\varepsilon\overline{e}_1+2k_1\overline{e}_2, \tag{5.3}$$

the Frenet-Cartan formulas (6.1) of Chapter I, with $P\Big|_{\sigma=0}=\overline{A}$.

The relation between the frame $(A, \overline{e}_1, \overline{e}_2)$ and the line (P) is known (§ 2 and § 3 of Chapter II). It remains to determine the relation between the vector $\overline{e}_3$ and the line (A) and point A. If the straight line (4.5) is known and the point E_1 is the end point of the vector $\overline{e}_1$, then the straight line passing through the point E_1 parallel to the binormal Ax^3 intersects the straight line (4.5) at the point Q with coordinates $\left(1;\ 0;\ \frac{5}{3}\right)$. The vertex R of the parallelogram AE_1QR has the coordinates $\left(0,\ 0,\ \frac{5}{3}\right)$.

The vector $\frac{3}{5}\overline{AR}$ will be the coordinate vector $\overline{e}_3$ if its origin lies at the point A.

We will say that the point A on the plane line (A) in space is a point of the hyperbolic, elliptic or parabolic type according as this point, with respect to the line (P), is a point of the hyperbolic, elliptic or parabolic type. The indefiniteness of the coordinate vectors at a point of the parabolic type on the plane line (§ 3, Chapter II) produces a similar indefiniteness of the coordinate vectors $\overline{e}_1, \overline{e}_2$ of the canonical frame $(A, \overline{e}_1, \overline{e}_2, \overline{e}_3)$ of the line in space (§4, Chapter III).

§ 6. **Curvatures.** The geometric interpretation of the curvature k_1, follows from formulas (5.3) (§ 4 of Chapter II).

For a geometric interpretation of the curvature k_2, let us obtain the equation of the characteristic of the family of normal planes of the line (A) on the plane x^2Ax^3. The equation of the family of normal planes of the line (A) is

$$|\overline{X}-\overline{A},\ \overline{e}_2,\ \overline{e}_3|=0, \tag{6.1}$$

if $A, \overline{e}_2, \overline{e}_3$ are regarded here as a vector function of σ.

Differentiating the determinant $|\overline{X}-\overline{A}, \overline{e}_1, \overline{e}_2|$ with respect to σ, using condition (6.1) and applying formulas (5.2) of Chapter III, we obtain the equation

$$|\overline{X}-\overline{A},\ \overline{e}_1,\ \overline{e}_3|+k_2|\overline{X}-\overline{A},\ e_2,\ \overline{e}_1|=|\overline{e}_1, \overline{e}_2, \overline{e}_3|. \tag{6.2}$$

For $\sigma = 0$, we obtain from equations (6.1–6.2) the equations of the required characteristic in the frame $(A, \overline{e}_1, \overline{e}_2, \overline{e}_3)$ in coordinate form

$$x^1 = 0; \quad x^2 + k_2 x^3 + 1 = 0. \tag{6.3}$$

It follows from equations (6.3) that: The characteristic of the family of normal planes of the line (A) on the plane x^2Ax^3 intersects the binormal Ax^3 at a point with coordinates $\left(0, 0, -\frac{1}{k_2}\right)$ and the principal normal at a point with coordinates (0, -1, 0).

§ 7. Exercises 1. Find the lines of zero curvature.

Answer:

$$\overline{A}(\sigma) = \sigma\overline{c}_1 + e^{2\sigma}\overline{c}_2 + e^{-2\sigma}\overline{c}_3 \quad (\varepsilon = 1);$$

$$\overline{A}(\sigma) = \sigma\overline{c}_1 + e^{\sqrt{2}\sigma}\overline{c}_2 + e^{-\sqrt{2}\sigma}\overline{c}_3 \quad (\varepsilon = -1);$$

$$\overline{A}(\sigma) = \sigma\overline{c}_1 + e^{\sqrt{3}\sigma}\overline{c}_2 + e^{-\sqrt{3}\sigma}\overline{c}_3 \quad (\varepsilon = 0).$$

2. Find the lines of constant curvature.

Answer:

$$\overline{A}(\sigma) = e^{h_1\sigma}\overline{c}_1 + e^{h_2\sigma}\overline{c}_2 + e^{h_3\sigma}\overline{c}_3;$$

$$\overline{A}(\sigma) = e^{\beta\sigma}\cos\alpha\sigma\overline{c}_1 + e^{\beta\sigma}\sin\alpha\sigma\overline{c}_2 + e^{h_3\sigma}\overline{c}_3;$$

$$\overline{A}(\sigma) = e^{h_1\sigma}\overline{c}_1 + \sigma e^{h_1\sigma}\overline{c}_2 + e^{h_3\sigma}\overline{c}_3;$$

$$\overline{A}(\sigma) = e^{h_1\sigma}\overline{c}_1 + \sigma e^{h_1\sigma}\overline{c}_2 + \sigma^2 e^{h_1\sigma}\overline{c}_3;$$

$$\overline{A}(\sigma) = \sigma\overline{c}_1 + e^{h_2\sigma}\overline{c}_2 + e^{h_3\sigma}\overline{c}_3;$$

$$\overline{A}(\sigma) = \sigma\overline{c}_1 + e^{h_2\sigma}\overline{c}_2 + \sigma e^{h_2\sigma}\overline{c}_3;$$

$$\overline{A}(\sigma) = \sigma\overline{c}_1 + e^{\beta\sigma}\cos\alpha\sigma\overline{c}_2 + e^{\beta\sigma}\sin\alpha\sigma\overline{c}_3;$$

$$\overline{A}(\sigma) = \sigma\overline{c}_1 + \sigma^2\overline{c}_2 + e^{h_3\sigma}\overline{c}_3;$$

$$\overline{A}(\sigma) = \sigma\overline{c}_1 + \sigma^2\overline{c}_2 + \sigma^3\overline{c}_3;$$

h_1, h_2, h_3 are nonzero.

Part Three
SURFACES

Chapter V

THE CANONICAL FRAME

§ 1. Fundamental relations. The surface (A) in three-dimensional affine space may be specified with reference to a certain frame in this space by the radius vector of the generic point A of the surface as a vector function of two independent scalar arguments u^1, u^2:

$$\overline{A} = \overline{A}(u^1, u^2). \tag{1.1}$$

The vector function $\overline{A}(u^1, u^2)$ is differentiable as many times as necessary for further discussion. The lines u^1 (u^2=const) and u^2 (u^1=const) will be the coordinate lines on this surface. The equations for infinitesimal displacements of the frame $(A, \overline{e}_1, \overline{e}_2, \overline{e}_3)$ (see Introduction) with origin at A and coordinate vectors $\overline{e}_1, \overline{e}_2, \overline{e}_3$ are:

$$d\overline{A} = \omega^i \overline{e}_i;\ d\overline{e}_i = \omega_i^j \overline{e}_j \quad (i, j, k = 1, 2, 3). \tag{1.2}$$

The equations of structure corresponding to the system (1.2) are:

$$D\omega^i = \left[\omega^j \omega_j^i\right];\ D\omega_i^j = \left[\omega_i^k \omega_k^i\right]. \tag{1.3}$$

§ 2. Frames of the first order. Frames with origin at the point A and coordinate vectors $\overline{e}_1, \overline{e}_2$ belonging to the tangent plane to the surface (A) at the point A – frames of the first order – are distinguished by the condition

$$d\overline{A} = \omega^1 \overline{e}_1 + \omega^2 \overline{e}_2, \tag{2.1}$$

or

$$\omega^3 = 0. \tag{2.2}$$

The forms ω^1 and ω^2 cannot be linearly dependent if the surface (A) has not degenerated into a line or a point. These forms are called principal and the remaining forms ω_i^j secondary.

§ 3. Continuation of the equation. By exterior differentiations of the form ω^3 under the condition (2.2) and use of Cartan's lemma, we obtain

$$\omega_{i_1}^3 = a_{i_1 i_2} \omega^{i_2} \quad (i_1, i_2, i_3 = 1, 2). \tag{3.1}$$

Continuing these equations, we obtain further

$$da_{i_1 i_2} = a_{i_3 i_1} \omega_{i_2}^{i_3} + a_{i_3 i_2} \omega_{i_1}^{i_3} - a_{i_1 i_2} \omega_3^3 + a_{i_1 i_2 i_3} \omega^{i_3}. \tag{3.2}$$

Continuing equations (3.2), simplifying and applying Cartan's lemma, we obtain

$$da_{i_1 i_2 i_3} = a_{i_4 i_1 i_2} \omega_{i_3}^{i_4} + a_{i_4 i_2 i_3} \omega_{i_1}^{i_4} + a_{i_4 i_3 i_1} \omega_{i_2}^{i_4} - a_{i_1 i_2 i_3} \omega_3^3 +$$
$$+ \left(a_{i_4 i_1} a_{i_2 i_3} + a_{i_4 i_2} a_{i_3 i_1} + a_{i_4 i_3} a_{i_1 i_2}\right) \omega_3^{i_4} + a_{i_1 i_2 i_3 i_4} \omega^{i_4}. \tag{3.3}$$

All the quantities $a_{i_1i_2}$, $a_{i_1i_2i_3}$, $a_{i_1i_2i_3i_4}$ are symmetric in the indices i_1, i_2, i_3, i_4:

$$\left.\begin{array}{l} a_{i_1i_2} = a_{i_2i_1};\ a_{i_1i_2i_3} = a_{i_2i_1i_3} = a_{i_1i_3i_2}, \\ a_{i_1i_2i_3i_4} = a_{i_2i_1i_3i_4} = a_{i_1i_3i_2i_4} = a_{i_1i_2i_4i_3}. \end{array}\right\} \tag{3.4}$$

§ 4. Conjugate and asymptotic directions. The equation of the tangent plane to the surface *(A)* at the point *A* can be written in the form of a determinant equated to zero:

$$|\overline{X} - \overline{A},\ \overline{e}_1,\ \overline{e}_2\,| = 0, \tag{4.1}$$

$\overline{X}-\overline{A}$ is the radius vector of the generic point X of the tangent plane in the frame $(A,\ \overline{e}_1,\ \overline{e}_2,\ \overline{e}_3)$.

On the surface *(A)* the line l_1 passing through the point A is specified by the equations:

$$u^1 = u^1(u);\ u^2 = u^2(u). \tag{4.2}$$

We will write the vector of the tangent to the line l_1 at the point A in the form

$$d_1\overline{A} = \underset{1}{\omega^1}\overline{e}_1 + \underset{1}{\omega^2}\overline{e}_2, \tag{4.3}$$

where

$$\underset{1}{\omega^i} = \omega^i\Big|_{u^k = u^k(u)} \quad (i,\ k = 1,\ 2). \tag{4.4}$$

At points on the line l_1, the tangent planes to the surface *(A)* constitute a one-parameter family the equation of which can be expressed in the form (4.1), assuming that here $A,\ \overline{e}_1,\ \overline{e}_2$ are vector functions of the parameter u which have been obtained with the help of equations (4.2). The characteristic of this family on the plane tangent to the surface *(A)* at the point $A(u_0^1,\ u_0^2)$ can be found by the simultaneous solution of equation (4.1) and the equation

$$\frac{d_1}{du}\left|\overline{X} - \overline{A},\ \overline{e}_1,\ \overline{e}_2\right| = 0 \tag{4.5}$$

for $u^1 = u_0^1$, $u^2 = u_0^2$.

The symbol d_1 indicates differentiation corresponding to displacement of the point A along the line l_1. After the differentiation indicated in equation (4.5) we obtain

$$|\overline{X} - \overline{A},\ d_1\overline{e}_1,\ \overline{e}_2| + |\overline{X} - \overline{A},\ \overline{e}_1,\ d_1\overline{e}_2\,| = 0; \tag{4.6}$$

$$d_1\overline{e}_i = \underset{1}{\omega_i^j}\overline{e}_j;\quad \underset{1}{\omega_i^j} = \omega_i^j\Big|_{u^k = u^k(u)}. \tag{4.7}$$

The vector $\overline{X}-\overline{A}$ belonging to the line of intersection of the planes specified by equations (4.1) and (4.6) will be written in the form

$$\overline{X} - \overline{A} = \underset{2}{\omega^1}\overline{e}_2 + \underset{2}{\omega^2}\overline{e}_2.$$

Therefore the condition of conjugation of the vector (4.3) and the vector

$$d_2\overline{A} = \underset{2}{\omega^1}\overline{e}_1 + \underset{2}{\omega^2}\overline{e}_2 \tag{4.8}$$

relative to the surface *(A)* at the point *A* is obtained in the form

$$\underset{2}{\omega^1}\,\underset{1}{\omega_1^3} + \underset{2}{\omega^2}\,\underset{1}{\omega_2^3} = 0. \tag{4.9}$$

After substitution of the forms $\underset{1}{\omega_1^3}$, $\underset{1}{\omega_2^3}$ by their expressions in equations (3.1), the condition of conjugation (4.9) can be written in the form

$$a_{11}\underset{1}{\omega^1}\underset{2}{\omega^1} + a_{12}\left(\underset{1}{\omega^1}\underset{2}{\omega^2} + \underset{2}{\omega^1}\underset{1}{\omega^2}\right) + a_{22}\underset{1}{\omega^2}\underset{2}{\omega^2} = 0. \tag{4.10}$$

From this it follows that the property of a vector of being conjugate with another relative to the surface at a point is reciprocal.

The coordinates of the vector $\omega^1\overline{e}_1+\omega^2\overline{e}_2$ with asymptotic direction relative to the surface *(A)* and the point *A* satisfy the equation

$$a_{11}\omega^{1^2} + 2a_{12}\omega^1\omega^2 + a_{22}\omega^{2^2} = 0. \tag{4.11}$$

Therefore the point *A* will be of the hyperbolic, elliptic or parabolic type according as

$$a_{12}^2 - a_{11}a_{22} > 0, \tag{4.12}$$

or

$$a_{12}^2 - a_{11}a_{22} < 0, \tag{4.13}$$

or

$$a_{12}^2 - a_{11}a_{22} = 0. \tag{4.14}$$

§ 5. Invariance of point, plane, quadric. Let the point *X* be specified in the frame $(A, \overline{e}_1, \overline{e}_2, \overline{e}_3)$:

$$\overline{AX} = x^i\overline{e}_i.$$

For infinitesimal displacement of the frame, the condition of invariance of the point *X* is:

$$d\overline{AX} = \left(dx^i + x^k\omega_k^i\right)\overline{e}_i,$$

or

$$dx^i = -x^k\omega_k^i. \tag{5.1}$$

Relative to the same frame, the equation of a plane is

$$a_ix^i + a = 0 \quad (i = 1, 2, 3). \tag{5.2}$$

For infinitesimal displacement of the frame $(A, \overline{e}_1, \overline{e}_2, \overline{e}_3)$ the condition of invariance of the plane (5.2) is:

$$(a_i + da_i)\left(x^i - x^k\omega_k^i\right) + a + da \approx (\Theta^0 + \Theta)(a_ix^i + a).$$

The symbol $\approx$ means that in the left- and right-hand members the expressions consisting of the first-order terms are equal, as are the individual terms of the first order of smallness with respect to a_i, a, x^i. Therefore

$$\Theta^0 = 1;$$

$$da_i = a_k\omega_i^k + \Theta a_i; \; da = \Theta a. \tag{5.3}$$

Equations (5.3) are the conditions of invariance of the plane (5.2).

The equation of the quadric (here a surface of the second order) in the frame $(A, \overline{e}_1, \overline{e}_2, \overline{e}_3)$ is:

$$A_{ij}x^ix^j + 2A_{0i}x^i + A_{00} = 0 \quad (i, j, k = 1, 2, 3). \tag{5.4}$$

For infinitesimal displacement of the frame, the condition of invariance of the quadric (5.4) is:

$$(A_{ij}+dA_{ij})\left(x^i-x^k\omega_k^i\right)\left(x^j-x^k\omega_k^j\right)+2\left(A_{0i}+dA_{0i}\right)\left(x^i-x^k\omega_k^i\right)$$
$$+A_{00}+dA_{00}\equiv(\Theta^0+\Theta)\left(A_{ij}x^ix^j+2A_{0i}x^i+A_{00}\right).$$

The quantity Θ^0 is of order zero and Θ of the first order. Consequently,

$$\Theta^0=1.$$

The conditions of invariance of the quadric (5.4) are:

$$\left.\begin{aligned} dA_{ij}&=A_{ik}\omega_s^k+A_{jk}\omega_i^k+\Theta A_{ij};\\ dA_{0i}&=A_{0k}\omega_i^k+\Theta A_{0i};\\ dA_{00}&=\Theta A_{00}. \end{aligned}\right\}\ (i,j,k=1,2,3) \tag{5.5}$$

After separation of the equations corresponding to the indices i_1, i_2, $i_3=1,\ 2$ and substitution of the forms $\omega_{i_1}{}^3$ by their expressions in equations (3.1), this system can be written in the form

$$\left.\begin{aligned} dA_{i_1i_2}&=A_{i_1i_3}\omega_{i_2}^{i_3}+A_{i_2i_3}\omega_{i_1}^{i_3}+\Theta A_{i_1i_2}+(A_{i_13}a_{i_2i_3}+A_{i_23}a_{i_1i_3})\,\omega^{i_3};\\ dA_{0i_1}&=A_{0i_2}\omega_{i_1}^{i_2}+\Theta A_{0i_1}+A_{03}a_{i_1i_2}\omega^{i_2};\\ dA_{00}&=\Theta A_{00};\\ dA_{03}&=A_{0i_1}\omega_3^{i_1}+\Theta A_{03}+A_{03}\omega_3^3;\\ dA_{i_13}&=A_{i_1i_2}\omega_3^{i_2}+A_{3i_2}\omega_{i_1}^{i_2}+\Theta A_{i_13}+A_{i_13}\omega_3^3+A_{33}a_{i_1i_2}\omega^{i_2};\\ dA_{33}&=2A_{3i_1}\omega_3^{i_1}+\Theta A_{33}+2A_{33}\omega_3^3\\ &\qquad(i_1,\ i_2,\ i_3=1,\ 2). \end{aligned}\right\} \tag{5.6}$$

§ 6. Fundamental quantity of the third order. The set of functions $a_{i_1i_2}$, $a_{i_1i_2i_3}$ defined by the system of differential equations (3.2–3.3) is called a fundamental geometric quantity of the third order associated with the surface (A) /6/.

We will consider only such surfaces at whose points

$$a=det\,|a_{i_1i_2}|\neq 0. \tag{6.1}$$

Let the functions $a^{i_1i_2}$ and $a_{i_1i_2}$ be related by

$$a^{i_1i_3}a_{i_3i_2}=\delta_{i_2}^{i_1}, \tag{6.2}$$

$\delta_{i_2}^{i_1}$ is the Kronecker symbol. From conditions (6.1) and

$$a_{i_1i_2}=a_{i_2i_1} \tag{6.3}$$

it follows that

$$a^{i_1i_2}=a_{i_2i_1}. \tag{6.4}$$

Differentiating both sides of equation (6.2), we obtain

$$(da^{i_1i_3})\,a_{i_3i_2}+a^{i_1i_3}da_{i_3i_2}=0.$$

Consequently,

$$da^{i_1i_2}=-a^{i_1i_3}a^{i_2i_4}da_{i_3i_4}.$$

Replacing $da_{i_3 i_4}$ in this equation by its expression (3.2), we obtain

$$da^{i_1 i_2} = -a^{i_1 i_3}\omega_{i_3}^{i_2} - a^{i_2 i_3}\omega_{i_3}^{i_1} + a^{i_1 i_2}\omega_3^3 - a^{i_1 i_3} a^{i_2 i_4} a_{i_3 i_4 i_5}\omega^{i_5}. \tag{6.5}$$

The differential of the determinant a of (6.1) can be written in the form

$$da = \tilde{a}^{i_1 i_2}\, da_{i_1 i_2}, \tag{6.6}$$

$\tilde{a}^{i_1 i_2}$ is the algebraic complement of the element a_{ij} of the determinant a:

$$\tilde{a}^{i_1 i_2} = a a^{i_1 i_2}. \tag{6.7}$$

Replacing $da_{i_1 i_2}$ by its expression in (3.2) and using the conditions (6.2), (6.7) equation (6.6) can be written in the form

$$da = 2a\left(\omega_1^1 + \omega_2^2 - \omega_3^3\right) + \tilde{a}^{i_1 i_2} a_{i_1 i_2 i_3}\omega^{i_3}. \tag{6.8}$$

Set

$$b_{i_1} = a^{i_2 i_3} a_{i_2 i_3 i_1}. \tag{6.9}$$

Using (6.7) and (6.9) equation (6.8) can be written as:

$$da = a\left[2\left(\omega_1^1 + \omega_2^2 - \omega_3^3\right) + b_{i_1}\omega^{i_1}\right]. \tag{6.10}$$

Differentiating both sides of equation (6.9), we obtain

$$db_{i_1} = (da^{i_2 i_3})\, a_{i_2 i_3 i_1} + a^{i_2 i_3} da_{i_2 i_3 i_1}. \tag{6.11}$$

Replacing $da^{i_2 i_3}$ and $da_{i_2 i_3 i_1}$ by their expressions in (6.5) and (3.3), we obtain

$$db_{i_1} = b_{i_2}\omega_{i_1}^{i_2} + 4a_{i_1 i_2}\omega_3^{i_2} + l_{i_1 i_2}\omega^{i_2}. \tag{6.12}$$

§ 7. Osculating quadrics. Let us assign to every point A of the surface (A) a quadric (surface of the second order) the equation of which in the local frame $(A, \bar{e}_1, \bar{e}_2, \bar{e}_3)$ has the form (5.4). The field of such quadrics is defined by the system of differential equations (5.5).

The condition that the point A belongs to the quadric (5.4) is:

$$A_{00} = 0. \tag{7.1}$$

The condition that, to infinitesimals of the first order, the point with radius vector $\bar{A} + d\bar{A}$ belongs to this quadric is:

$$A_{ij}\,\omega^i\omega^j + 2A_{0i}\omega^i = 0.$$

Assuming that in this equation $\omega^3 = 0$ and ω^1, ω^2 are arbitrary, we obtain

$$A_{01} = 0, \quad A_{02} = 0. \tag{7.2}$$

We will demand that the coefficient

$$A_{03} = -1. \tag{7.3}$$

For the conditions (7.1–7.3), we find from equations (5.5) that:

$$\Theta = -\omega_3^3; \tag{7.4}$$

$$\left.\begin{aligned} dA_{i_1 i_2} &= A_{i_1 i_3}\omega_{i_2}^{i_3} + A_{i_2 i_3}\omega_{i_1}^{i_2} - A_{i_1 i_2}\omega_3^3 + \left(A_{i_1 3} a_{i_2 i_3} + A_{i_2 3} a_{i_1 i_3}\right)\omega^{i_3};\\ dA_{i_1 3} &= A_{i_2 3}\,\omega_{i_1}^{i_2} + A_{i_1 i_2}\omega_3^{i_2} + A_{33}\, a_{i_1 i_2}\omega^{i_2};\\ dA_{33} &= 2A_{3 i_1}\omega_3^{i_1} + A_{33}\omega_3^3. \end{aligned}\right\} \tag{7.5}$$

Let us now pick out those such quadrics (5.4) which contain the point $A(u^1, u^2)$ of the surface (A), with an accuracy to infinitesimals of the second order relative to ω^1 and ω^2. We have

$$\overline{A} + d\overline{A} + \frac{1}{2} d^2\overline{A} = \left[\omega^{i_1} + \frac{1}{2}\left(d\omega^{i_1} + \omega^{i_2}\omega_{i_2}^{i_1}\right)\right]\overline{e}_1 + \frac{1}{2} a_{i_1 i_2}\omega^{i_1}\omega^{i_2}\overline{e}_3.$$

The requirement that, to infinitesimals of the second order, a point with such a radius vector belong to the quadric (5.4) for conditions (7.1–7.3) and $\omega^3 = 0$ reduces to the requirement of the identity

$$A_{i_1 i_2}\left[\omega^{i_1} + \frac{1}{2}\left(d\omega^{i_1} + \omega^{i_3}\omega_{i_3}^{i_1}\right)\right]\left[\omega^{i_2} + \frac{1}{2}\left(d\omega^{i_2} + \omega^{i_3}\omega_{i_3}^{i_2}\right)\right] -$$
$$- a_{i_1 i_2}\omega^{i_1}\omega^{i_2} \equiv 0$$

up to infinitesimals of the second order, or

$$A_{i_1 i_2} = a_{i_1 i_2}. \tag{7.6}$$

We note that the above corresponds to the identity of the differential equations (3.2) and (7.5 : 1). If we set

$$b_{i_1} = 4A_{i_1 3}, \tag{7.7}$$

then the differential equations (6.12) and (7.5 : 2) will be the same. Replacing the coefficients in equation (5.4) by their values in (7.1–7.3), (7.6–7.7), we obtain the equation of a Darboux pencil of osculating quadrics

$$a_{i_1 i_2}x^{i_1}x^{i_2} - 2x^3 + \frac{b_{i_1}}{2} x^{i_1}x^3 + A_{33}{x^3}^2 = 0. \tag{7.8}$$

§ 8. Choice of the canonical frame. Set

$$a_{11} = \alpha; \; a_{12} = 0; \; a_{22} = 1, \tag{8.1}$$

$\alpha = 1$ if the point A is of the elliptic type and $\alpha = -1$ if it is of the hyperbolic type.

Points of the parabolic type ($\alpha = 0$) are excluded from the present discussion. From equations (3.1–3.2), (6.2), (6.9) we obtain with (8.1)

$$\omega_1^3 = \alpha\omega^1; \quad \omega_2^3 = \omega^2; \tag{8.2}$$

$$\left.\begin{aligned} &\alpha\left(2\omega_1^1 - \omega_3^3\right) + a_{11i_1}\omega^{i_1} = 0;\\ &\alpha\omega_2^1 + \omega_1^2 + a_{12i_1}\omega^{i_1} = 0;\\ &2\omega_2^2 - \omega_3^3 + a_{22i_1}\omega^{i_1} = 0; \end{aligned}\right\} \tag{8.3}$$

$$a^{11} = \frac{1}{\alpha}, \; a^{12} = 0, \; a^{22} = 1;$$

$$b_1 = \frac{1}{\alpha} a_{111} + a_{221}, \quad b_2 = \frac{1}{\alpha} a_{112} + a_{222}. \tag{8.4}$$

We now set

$$b_1 = 0; \; b_2 = 0. \tag{8.5}$$

From equations (8.4) we obtain:

$$a_{111} + \alpha a_{122} = 0; \; a_{112} + \alpha a_{222} = 0. \tag{8.6}$$

Set

$$a_{222}=0;\ a_{122}=-1. \tag{8.7}$$

From equations (8.6), (8.3) and (3.3) we obtain, using (8.7):

$$a_{111}=\alpha;\ a_{112}=0; \tag{8.8}$$

$$\left.\begin{aligned}\omega_1^1&=\frac{1}{2}\omega_3^3-\frac{1}{2}\omega^1;\\ \omega_2^1&=-\alpha\omega_1^2+\alpha\omega^2;\\ \omega_2^2&=\frac{1}{2}\omega_3^3+\frac{1}{2}\omega^1.\end{aligned}\right\} \tag{8.9}$$

$$\left.\begin{aligned}&\alpha\left(3\omega_1^1-\omega_3^3\right)+3\omega_3^1+a_{111i_1}\omega^{i_1}=0;\\ &\alpha\omega_2^1-2\omega_1^2+\alpha\omega_3^2+a_{112i_1}\omega^{i_1}=0;\\ &\omega_3^3-\omega_1^1-2\omega_2^2+\alpha\omega_3^1+a_{122i_1}\omega^{i_1}=0;\\ &3\omega_3^2-3\omega_2^1+a_{222i_1}\omega^{i_1}=0.\end{aligned}\right\} \tag{8.10}$$

Replacing the forms ω_1^1. ω_2^1, ω_2^2 in equations (8.10) by their expressions in (8.9), we obtain

$$\left.\begin{aligned}&\frac{\alpha}{2}\omega_3^3+3\omega_3^1=\frac{3\alpha}{2}\omega^1-a_{111i_1}\omega^{i_1};\\ &3\omega_1^2-\alpha\omega_3^2=\omega^2+a_{112i_1}\omega^{i_1};\\ &\alpha\omega_3^1-\frac{1}{2}\omega_3^3=\frac{1}{2}\omega^1-a_{122i_1}\omega^{i_1};\\ &3\omega_3^2+3\alpha\omega_1^2=3\alpha\omega^2-a_{222i_1}\omega^{i_1}.\end{aligned}\right\} \tag{8.11}$$

Solving equation (8.11) for ω_3^3, ω_3^1, ω_1^2, ω_3^2 and introducing the expressions obtained for the latter into equations (8.9), we obtain

$$\left.\begin{aligned}\omega_1^1&=\frac{3a_{122i_1}-\alpha a_{111i_1}}{4}\omega^{i_1}-\frac{1}{2}\omega^1;\\ \omega_1^2&=\frac{1}{2}\omega^2+\frac{3a_{112i_1}-\alpha a_{222i_1}}{12}\omega^{i_1};\\ \omega_2^1&=\frac{\alpha}{2}\omega^2-\frac{3\alpha a_{112i_1}-a_{222i_1}}{12}\omega^{i_1};\\ \omega_2^2&=\frac{1}{2}\omega^1+\frac{3a_{122i_1}-\alpha a_{111i_1}}{4}\omega^{i_1};\\ \omega_3^1&=\frac{\alpha}{2}\omega^1-\frac{a_{111i_1}+\alpha a_{122i_1}}{4}\omega^{i_1};\\ \omega_3^2&=\frac{\alpha}{2}\omega^2-\frac{a_{222i_1}+\alpha a_{112i_1}}{4}\omega^{i_1};\\ \omega_3^3&=\frac{3a_{122i_1}-\alpha a_{111i_1}}{2}\omega^{i_1}.\end{aligned}\right\} \tag{8.12}$$

Let us introduce the new differential invariants p_1, p_2, p_3, q_1, q_2, related to the components of the fundamental geometric quantity of the fourth order for the surface (A), i.e., to the functions $a_{i_1i_2}$, $a_{i_1i_2i_3}$, $a_{i_1i_2i_3i_4}$, by the equations:

$$\left.\begin{aligned}&4p_1+a_{1111}+\alpha a_{1122}=0;\\ &4p_2+a_{1112}+\alpha a_{1222}=0;\\ &4p_3+a_{2222}+\alpha a_{1122}=0;\\ &4q_1=3a_{1122}-\alpha a_{1111};\\ &4q_2=3a_{1222}-\alpha a_{1112}.\end{aligned}\right\} \tag{8.13}$$

Replacing the components $a_{i_1 i_2 i_3 i_4}$ in equations (8.12) by their expressions as obtained from equations (8.13), we obtain

$$\left.\begin{aligned}
\omega_1^1 &= \left(q_1 - \frac{1}{2}\right)\omega^1 + q_2\omega^2;\\
\omega_1^2 &= -\frac{2p_2 + aq_2}{3}\omega^1 + \left(\frac{1}{2} + \frac{q_1 - ap_1 + ap_3}{3}\right)\omega^2;\\
\omega_2^1 &= \frac{2ap_2 + q_2}{3}\omega^1 + \left(\frac{a}{2} - \frac{aq_1 - p_1 + p_3}{3}\right)\omega^2;\\
\omega_2^2 &= \left(q_1 + \frac{1}{2}\right)\omega^1 + q_2\omega^2;\\
\omega_3^1 &= \left(\frac{a}{2} + p_1\right)\omega^1 + p_2\omega^2;\\
\omega_3^2 &= ap_2\omega^1 + \left(\frac{a}{2} + p_3\right)\omega^2;\\
\omega_3^3 &= 2q_1\omega^1 + 2q_2\omega^2.
\end{aligned}\right\} \tag{8.14}$$

All secondary forms ω_i^j in equations (8.2) and (8.14) refer to a ring with a basis consisting of the principal forms ω^1, ω^2. The canonical frame has been chosen.

§ 9. Darboux-Cartan formulas. Replacing all secondary forms in equations (1.2) by their expressions in equations (8.2) and (8.14) and setting $\omega^3 = 0$, we obtain the equations for infinitesimal displacements of the chosen canonical frame of the surface (A) in the form

$$\left.\begin{aligned}
d\bar{A} &= \omega^1\bar{e}_1 + \omega^2\bar{e}_2;\\
d\bar{e}_1 &= \left[\left(q_1 - \frac{1}{2}\right)\omega^1 + q_2\omega^2\right]\bar{e}_1 + \left[-\frac{2p_2 + aq_2}{3}\omega^1 + \right.\\
&\quad \left. + \left(\frac{1}{2} + \frac{q_1 - ap_1 + ap_3}{3}\right)\right]\bar{e}_2 + a\omega^1\bar{e}_3;\\
d\bar{e}_2 &= \left[\frac{2ap_2 + q_2}{3}\omega^1 + \left(\frac{a}{2} - \frac{aq_1 - p_1 + p_3}{3}\right)\omega^2\right]\bar{e}_1 +\\
&\quad + \left[\left(q_1 + \frac{1}{2}\right)\omega^1 + q_2\omega^2\right]\bar{e}_2 + \omega^2\bar{e}_3;\\
d\bar{e}_3 &= \left[\left(\frac{a}{2} + p_1\right)\omega^1 + p_2\omega^2\right]\bar{e}_1 + \left[ap_2\omega^1 + \right.\\
&\quad \left. + \left(\frac{a}{2} + p_3\right)\omega^2\right]\bar{e}_2 + (2q_1\omega^1 + 2q_2\omega^2)\bar{e}_3.
\end{aligned}\right\} \tag{9.1}$$

The equations of structure corresponding to the system (9.1) can be obtained by making use of formulas (1.3 : 2) and (9.1) in the form

$$\left.\begin{aligned}
D\omega^1 &= \frac{2}{3}(q_2 - ap_2)[\omega^1\omega^2];\ D\omega^2 =\\
&= \frac{1}{3}(ap_3 - ap_1 - 2q_1)[\omega^1\omega^2];\\
[dq_1\omega^1] + [dq_2\omega^2] &= \frac{a}{3}\{2p_2q_1 + q_2(p_1 - p_3)\}[\omega^1\omega^2];\\
[2dp_2 + adq_2, \omega^1] &- [dq_1 - adp_1 + adp_3, \omega^2] =\\
= \frac{1}{3}\{p_1^2 &+ 4ap_2^2 + p_3^2 - 2q_1^2 - 2aq_2^2 - 2p_2q_2 - ap_3q_1 +\\
&+ ap_1q_1 - 2p_1p_3 - \frac{9a}{2}(p_1 + p_3)\}[\omega^1\omega^2];
\end{aligned}\right\} \tag{9.2}$$

$$\left.\begin{aligned}&[dp_1\omega^1]+[dp_2\omega^2]+\Big(aq_2-p_2+\frac{5}{3}p_1q_2-\frac{4}{3}ap_1p_2+\\&\quad+\frac{4}{3}ap_1p_3-\frac{4}{3}p_2q_1+\frac{1}{3}p_3q_2\Big)[\omega^1\omega^2];\\&[adp_2\omega^1]+[dp_3\omega^2]+\Big\{\frac{4}{3}ap_2q_2-\frac{4}{3}p_2^2+\frac{1}{2}p_3-\\&\quad-\frac{1}{2}p_1-aq_1+\frac{a}{3}p_3^2-\frac{2}{3}ap_1p_3-\frac{5}{3}p_3q_1-\\&\quad-\frac{p_1}{3}(q_1-ap_1)\Big\}[\omega^1\omega^2]=0.\end{aligned}\right\}\tag{9.2}$$

§ 10. Canonical expansions of the coordinates of the generic point of the surface. Expanding the vector function $\overline{A}(\omega^1, \omega^2)$ in the neighborhood of the point $A(0, 0)$ in a Maclaurin series, we obtain

$$\overline{A}(\omega^1,\omega^2)=\overline{A}+d\overline{A}+\frac{1}{2}d^2\overline{A}+\frac{1}{6}d^3\overline{A}+\overline{R}(4).\tag{10.1}$$

The symbol $R(4)$ denotes the remainder of this series starting from $\frac{1}{4!}d^4\overline{A}$.

Using the conditions (9.1) we obtain:

$$\left.\begin{aligned}&d\overline{A}=\omega^1\overline{e}_1+\omega^2\overline{e}_2;\\&d^2\overline{A}=\Big[d\omega^1+\Big(q_1-\frac{1}{2}\Big)\omega^{1^2}+\frac{2}{3}(ap_2+2q_2)\omega^1\omega^2+\\&+\Big(\frac{a}{2}-\frac{aq_1-p_1+p_3}{3}\Big)\omega^{2^2}\Big]\overline{e}_1+\Big[d\omega^2-\frac{1}{3}(2p_2+aq_2)\omega^{1^2}+\\&+\Big(1+\frac{4q_1-ap_1+ap_3}{3}\Big)\omega^1\omega^2+q_2\omega^{2^2}\Big]\overline{e}_2+(a\omega^{1^2}+\omega^{2^2})\overline{e}_3;\\&d^3\overline{A}=a^1\overline{e}_1+a^2\overline{e}_2+\Big[3(a\omega^1d\omega^1+\omega^2d\omega^2)+a\Big(3q_1-\frac{1}{2}\Big)\omega^{1^3}+\\&\quad+3aq_2\omega^{1^2}\omega^2+3\Big(\frac{1}{2}+q_1\Big)\omega^1\omega^{2^2}+3q_2\omega^{2^3}\Big]\overline{e}_3.\end{aligned}\right\}\tag{10.2}$$

The symbols a^1 and a^2 denote the coefficients of $\overline{e}_1$ and $\overline{e}_2$. Replacing $d\overline{A}$, $d^2\overline{A}$, $d^3\overline{A}$ in equation (10.1) by their expressions in (10.2), we obtain the equation of the surface (A) in the frame $(A, \overline{e}_1, \overline{e}_2, \overline{e}_3)$ in the form

$$\begin{aligned}&A(\omega^1,\omega^2)=\Big\{\omega^1+\frac{1}{2}\Big[d\omega^1+\Big(q_1-\frac{1}{2}\Big)\omega^{1^2}+\frac{2}{3}(ap_2+2q_2)\omega^1\omega^2+\\&+\Big(\frac{a}{2}-\frac{aq_1-p_1+p_3}{3}\Big)\omega^{2^2}\Big]+\ldots\Big\}\overline{e}_1+\Big\{\omega^2+\frac{1}{2}\Big[d\omega^2-\\&-\frac{1}{3}(2p_2+aq_2)\omega^{1^2}+\Big(1+\frac{4q_1-ap_1+ap_3}{3}\Big)\omega^1\omega^2+q_2\omega^{2^2}\Big]+\ldots\Big\}\overline{e}_2+\\&+\Big\{\frac{1}{2}(a\omega^{1^2}+\omega^{2^2})+\frac{1}{6}\Big[3(a\omega^1d\omega^1+\omega^2d\omega^2)+a\Big(3q_1-\frac{1}{2}\Big)\omega^{1^3}+\\&+3aq_2\omega^{1^2}\omega^2+3\Big(\frac{1}{2}+q_1\Big)\omega^1\omega^{2^2}+3q_2\omega^{2^3}\Big]+\ldots\Big\}\overline{e}_3.\end{aligned}\tag{10.3}$$

If x^1, x^2, x^3 are the current coordinates of the point A (ω^1, ω^2) in the frame $(A, \bar{e}_1, \bar{e}_2, \bar{e}_3)$, then from equation (10.3) we obtain

$$\left.\begin{aligned} x^1 &= \omega^1 + \frac{1}{2}\left[d\omega^1 + \left(q_1 - \frac{1}{2}\right)\omega^{1^2} + \frac{2}{3}(\alpha p_2 + 2q_2)\,\omega^1\omega^2 + \right. \\ &\quad \left. + \left(\frac{\alpha}{2} - \frac{\alpha q_1 - p_1 + p_3}{3}\right)\omega^{2^2}\right] + \dots \\ x^2 &= \omega^2 + \frac{1}{2}\left[d\omega^2 - \frac{1}{3}(2p_2 + \alpha q_2)\,\omega^{1^2} + \left(1 + \right.\right. \\ &\quad \left.\left. + \frac{4q_1 - \alpha p_1 + \alpha p_3}{3}\right)\omega^1\omega^2 + q_2\omega^{2^2}\right] + \dots \\ x^3 &= \frac{1}{2}\left[\left(\alpha\omega^{1^2} + \omega^{2^2}\right) + \alpha\omega^1 d\omega^1 + \omega^2 d\omega^2 + \alpha\left(q_1 - \frac{1}{6}\right)\omega^{1^3} + \right. \\ &\quad \left. + \alpha q_2 \omega^{1^2}\omega^2 + \left(\frac{1}{2} + q_1\right)\omega^1\omega^{2^2} + q_2\omega^{2^3}\right] + \dots \end{aligned}\right\} \qquad (10.4)$$

Let us write the equation of the surface (A) in the form

$$x^3 = a_1 x^{1^2} + a_2 x^1 x^2 + a_3 x^{2^2} + b_1 x^{1^3} + b_2 x^{1^2} x^2 + b_3 x^1 x^{2^2} + \\ + b_4 x^{2^3} + 0\,(4). \qquad (10.5)$$

Replacing the coordinates x^1, x^2, x^3 in equation (10.5) by their expressions in (10.4) and comparing the infinitesimals up to the fourth order in the identity we have obtained, we find that

$$a_1 = \frac{\alpha}{2};\ \ a_2 = 0;\ \ a_3 = \frac{1}{2};\ \ b_1 = \frac{\alpha}{3};\ \ b_2 = b_3 = b_4 = 0.$$

We obtain the equation of the surface (A) in the form

$$x^3 = \frac{1}{2}\left(\alpha x^{1^2} + x^{2^2}\right) + \frac{\alpha}{3} x^{1^3} + 0\,(4). \qquad (10.6)$$

Chapter VI

RELATION BETWEEN THE CANONICAL FRAME AND THE SURFACE

§ 1. Osculating paraboloid. Retaining only the principal terms in the right-hand sides of equation (10.4) of Chapter V, we obtain the equation of the surface:

$$x^1 = \omega^1;\ \ x^2 = \omega^2;\ \ 2x^3 = \alpha\omega^{1^2} + \omega^{2^2}. \qquad (1.1)$$

Eliminating the forms ω^1 and ω^2, we obtain the equation of this surface in implicit form:

$$2x^3 = \alpha x^{1^2} + x^{2^2}. \qquad (1.2)$$

This surface is the osculating elliptic or hyperbolic paraboloid to the surface (A) at the point A if $\alpha = 1$ or $\alpha = -1$.

§ 2. Pencil of Darboux quadrics. Equation (7.8) of Chapter V for the pencil of Darboux quadrics is, taking into account the conditions (8.1), (8.5) of Chapter V,

$$\alpha x^{1^2} + x^{2^2} - 2x^3 + A_{33} x^{3^2} = 0. \qquad (2.1)$$

The presence of the single free parameter A_{33} means that the surface of the pencil (2.1) is the limiting position of a surface of second order having a common point A with the surface (A) and seven other independent common points when the latter coincide with the point A.

To the remaining ninth common point of the surface of the pencil (2.1) and surface (A) corresponds the last, still unused condition (7.5 : 3) of Chapter V.

In conformity with equations (7.7), (8.5) of Chapter V, it can be written in the form

$$dA_{33} = A_{33}\omega_2^3. \tag{2.2}$$

To the solution of equation (2.2)

$$A_{33} = 0$$

corresponds a completely osculating Darboux quadric, the osculating paraboloid (1.2).

§ 3. Affine normal. From equation (2.1) it follows that the affine normal to the surface (A) at the point A contains the locus of the centers of the osculating Darboux quadrics at this point. It is the diameter of the Darboux quadric which passes through the point A and is conjugate to the tangent plane to the surface (A) at the point A.

§ 4. Conjugate normal planes. The vector

$$d_c\overline{A} = \omega^2\overline{e}_1 - a\omega^1\overline{e}_2, \tag{4.1}$$

is conjugate to the vector

$$d\overline{A} = \omega^1\overline{e}_1 + \omega^2\overline{e}_2 \tag{4.2}$$

relative to the surface (A) and the point A in conformity with conditions (4.9) and (8.2) of Chapter V.

Corollary. If the first vector is conjugate to the second, then the second is conjugate to the first relative to the same surface and the same point.

The normal plane is said to be conjugate to the vector (4.2) relative to the surface (A) and the point A if it passes through the vector (4.1). We will say that the first of these planes is conjugate to the second. The property of conjugation of two such planes is reciprocal.

All these concepts are commonplace for a Darboux quadric conjugate to the surface (A) at the point A.

§ 5. Lines on the surface. By the coordinate line σ^1 on the surface (A) we will mean the line at every point of which the vector $\overline{e}_1$ of the canonical frame is tangent to this line; at every point of the line σ^2 the vector $\overline{e}_2$ of the same frame is tangent to it.

The pair of numbers (σ^1, σ^2) will be a pair of curvilinear coordinates of a point on the surface. The principal forms ω^1, ω^2 will have the form

$$\omega^1 = a^1(\sigma^1, \sigma^2)\, d\sigma^1;\quad \omega^2 = a^2(\sigma^1, \sigma^2)\, d\sigma^2. \tag{5.1}$$

A line on the surface can be specified by equations in the parametric form

$$\sigma^1 = \sigma^1(\sigma);\quad \sigma^2 = \sigma^2(\sigma). \tag{5.2}$$

At points on this line

$$\left.\begin{aligned} &\omega^\alpha \Big| \sigma^1(\sigma), \sigma^2(\sigma) = \lambda^\alpha d\sigma;\quad \alpha, \beta = 1, 2 \\ &\omega_i^j \Big| \sigma^1(\sigma), \sigma^2(\sigma) = \lambda_i^j(\sigma)\, d\sigma;\quad \frac{d\overline{e}_i}{d\sigma} = \lambda_i^j \overline{e}_j. \end{aligned}\right\} \tag{5.3}$$

Equations (9.1) of Chapter V can be written in the form

$$\left.\begin{aligned}
\frac{d\bar{A}}{d\sigma} &= \lambda^1 \bar{e}_1 + \lambda^2 \bar{e}_2; \\
\frac{d\bar{e}_1}{d\sigma} &= \left[\left(q_1 - \frac{1}{2}\right)\lambda^1 + q_2\lambda^2\right]\bar{e}_1 + \left[-\frac{2p_2 + aq_2}{3}\lambda^1 + \right.\\
&\quad \left. + \left(\frac{1}{2} + \frac{q_1 - ap_1 + ap_3}{3}\right)\lambda^2\right]\bar{e}_2 + a\lambda^1 \bar{e}_3; \\
\frac{d\bar{e}_2}{d\sigma} &= \left[\frac{2ap_2 + q_2}{3}\lambda^1 + \left(\frac{a}{2} - \frac{aq_1 - p_1 + p_3}{3}\right)\lambda^2\right]\bar{e}_1 + \\
&\quad + \left[\left(q_1 + \frac{1}{2}\right)\lambda^1 + q_2\lambda^2\right]\bar{e}_2 + \lambda^2 \bar{e}_3; \\
\frac{d\bar{e}_3}{d\sigma} &= \left[\left(\frac{a}{2} + p_1\right)\lambda^1 + p_2\lambda^2\right]\bar{e}_1 + \left[ap_2\lambda^1 + \left(\frac{a}{2} + p_3\right)\lambda^2\right]\bar{e}_2 + \\
&\quad + 2(q_1\lambda^1 + q_2\lambda^2)\bar{e}_3.
\end{aligned}\right\} \qquad (5.4)$$

Here the functions p , p_2, p_3, q_1, q_2 depend on σ.

If the osculating plane of this line at the point A passes through the normal Ax^3, then the determinant

$$\left|\bar{e}_3, \frac{d\bar{A}}{d\sigma}, \frac{d^2\bar{A}}{d\sigma^2}\right| = 0. \qquad (5.5)$$

Differentiating the derivative $\frac{d\bar{A}}{d\sigma}$ with respect to σ and using equations (8.2) of Chapter V and (5.3), we obtain

$$\begin{aligned}
\frac{d^2\bar{A}}{d\sigma^2} &= \left(\frac{d\lambda^1}{d\sigma} + \lambda^1\lambda^1_1 + \lambda^2\lambda^1_2\right)\bar{e}_1 + \left(\frac{d\lambda^2}{d\sigma} + \lambda^1\lambda^2_1 + \lambda^2\lambda^2_2\right)\bar{e}_2 + \\
&\quad + \left(a\lambda^{1^2} + \lambda^{2^2}\right)\bar{e}_3.
\end{aligned} \qquad (5.6)$$

Therefore the condition (5.5) can be written in the form

$$\left.\begin{aligned}
\frac{d\lambda^1}{d\sigma} + \lambda^1\lambda^1_1 + \lambda^2\lambda^1_2 &= \varphi\lambda^1; \\
\frac{d\lambda^2}{d\sigma} + \lambda^1\lambda^2_1 + \lambda^2\lambda^2_2 &= \varphi\lambda^2.
\end{aligned}\right\} \qquad (5.7)$$

The vector conjugate to the vector

$$\frac{d\bar{A}}{d\sigma} = \lambda^1 \bar{e}_1 + \lambda^2 \bar{e}_2 \qquad (5.8)$$

relative to the surface (A) and the point A, in conformity with formula (4.1), is

$$\frac{d_c\bar{A}}{d\sigma} = \lambda^2 \bar{e}_1 - a\lambda^1 \bar{e}_2. \qquad (5.9)$$

§ 6. Family of planes conjugate to the tangents to the normal section of the surface. The equation of the normal plane conjugate to the vector (5.8) and the radius vector $\bar{X}$ of the generic point X of this plane can be written as a determinant equated to zero

$$\left|\bar{X} - \bar{A}, \bar{e}_3, \frac{d_c\bar{A}}{d\sigma}\right| = 0. \qquad (6.1)$$

The derivative in the above is defined by formula (5.9). If the point A describes the normal section on the surface (A), then equation (6.1) can be regarded as the equation for a one-parameter family of planes. Let us find the characteristic of this family on the plane corresponding to the fixed point A. Differentiating both sides of equation (6.1) with respect to σ and making use of formulas (5.3) and (5.9), we obtain

$$\left|\overline{X}-\overline{A},\ \lambda_3^i\overline{e}_i,\ \lambda^2\overline{e}_1-\alpha\lambda^1\overline{e}_2\right|+\left|\overline{X}-\overline{A},\ \overline{e}_3,\ \frac{d\lambda^2}{d\sigma}\overline{e}_1-\alpha\frac{d\lambda^1}{d\sigma}\overline{e}_2+\right.$$
$$\left.+\left(\lambda^2\lambda_1^i-\alpha\lambda^1\lambda_2^i\right)\overline{e}_i\right|=\left|\lambda^1\overline{e}_1+\lambda^2\overline{e}_2,\ \overline{e}_3,\ \lambda^2\overline{e}_1-\alpha\lambda^1\overline{e}_2\right|. \quad (6.2)$$

We express the radius vector $\overline{X}-\overline{A}$ of the point X of this surface in the frame $(A, \overline{e}_1, \overline{e}_2, \overline{e}_3)$ in the form

$$\overline{X}-\overline{A}=x^i\overline{e}_i. \quad (6.3)$$

Therefore the equation of the plane (6.2) in the coordinates of the frame $(A, \overline{e}_1, \overline{e}_2, \overline{e}_3)$ is

$$\left(\alpha\frac{d\lambda^1}{d\sigma}-\lambda^2\lambda_1^2+\alpha\lambda^1\lambda_2^2+\alpha\lambda^1\lambda_3^3\right)x^1+\left(\frac{d\lambda^2}{d\sigma}+\lambda^2\lambda_1^1-\alpha\lambda^1\lambda_2^1+\lambda^2\lambda_3^3\right)x^2-$$
$$-\left(\alpha\lambda^1\lambda_3^1+\lambda^2\lambda_3^2\right)x^3=\alpha\lambda^{1^2}+\lambda^{2^2}. \quad (6.4)$$

Replacing $\frac{d\lambda^1}{d\sigma}$ and $\frac{d\lambda^2}{d\sigma}$ in the above by their expressions from the conditions (5.7) and $\lambda_1^2, \lambda_2^2, \lambda_3^3, \lambda_1^1, \lambda_2^1$ by their expressions from the system (5.4), we obtain

$$\left[\alpha\varphi\lambda^1+\alpha(2q_1+1)\lambda^{1^2}+2\alpha q_2\lambda^1\lambda^2-\lambda^{2^2}\right]x^1+\left[\varphi\lambda^2+2(q_1-1)\lambda^1\lambda^2+\right.$$
$$\left.+2q_2\lambda^{2^2}\right]x^2-\left(\alpha\lambda^1\lambda_3^1+\lambda^2\lambda_3^2\right)x^3=\alpha\lambda^{1^2}+\lambda^{2^2}. \quad (6.5)$$

The equation of the plane (6.1) corresponding to the fixed point A in the coordinates of the frame $(A, \overline{e}_1, \overline{e}_2, \overline{e}_3)$ is:

$$\alpha\lambda^1x^1+\lambda^2x^2=0. \quad (6.6)$$

The required characteristic is the straight line of intersection of the planes the equations of which are (6.5) and (6.6).

We obtain the point of intersection of this characteristic and the tangent plane to the surface (A) at the point A by adjoining to equations (6.5–6.6) the equation

$$x^3=0. \quad (6.7)$$

The equations of this line in parametric form are

$$x^1=\frac{\alpha\lambda^{1^2}+\lambda^{2^2}}{3\alpha\lambda^{1^2}-\lambda^{2^2}};\quad x^2=-\alpha\frac{\lambda^1}{\lambda^2}\frac{\alpha\lambda^{1^2}+\lambda^{2^2}}{3\alpha\lambda^{1^2}-\lambda^{2^2}};\quad x^3=0. \quad (6.8)$$

Here the ratio $\frac{\lambda^1}{\lambda^2}$ can be taken as the parameter. Eliminating the parameter $\lambda^1:\lambda^2$ from equations (6.8), we obtain the equation of the line under consideration in implicit form in the plane x^1Ax^2:

$$x^1\left(3x^{2^2}-\alpha x^{1^2}\right)=\alpha x^{1^2}+x^{2^2}. \quad (6.9)$$

This is a line of the third order. We will call it the indicatrix of the characteristics of the normal planes of the surface (A) corresponding to the point A. The origin of coordinates is a singular point of the indicatrix (6.9). The indicatrix (6.9) is the intersection of the plane x^1Ax^2 and the ruled surface formed by the indicated characteristics that correspond to all displacements (5.8). Equations (6.5) and (6.6) with the conditions (5.7) are the equations of this ruled surface in parametric form. Here the ratio $\lambda^1 : \lambda^2$ is the parameter.

§ 7. Diagram of the indicatrix of the characteristics of the normal planes. The equation of the indicatrix (6.9) corresponding to a point A of the elliptic type ($\alpha=1$) is:

$$x^1 (3x^{2^2} - x^{1^2}) = x^{1^2} + x^{2^2}. \qquad (7.1)$$

Any straight line given by the equation

$$x^2 = hx^1, \qquad (7.2)$$

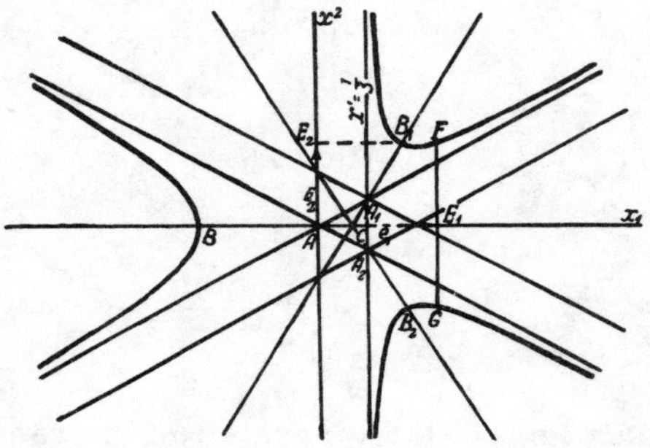

FIGURE 1

from the pencil of straight lines with center A intersects the line (7.1) (aside from the isolated point A) at the point with the coordinates

$$x^1 = \frac{h^2+1}{3h^2-1}; \quad x^2 = h\,\frac{h^2+1}{3h^2-1}. \qquad (7.3)$$

It follows from these equations that the straight lines

$$x^2 = \frac{1}{\sqrt{3}}x^1; \quad x^2 = -\frac{1}{\sqrt{3}}x^1; \quad x^1 = \frac{1}{3} \qquad (7.4)$$

are asymptotes of the line (7.1). The indicatrix under consideration consists of three branches shown in Figure 1. The coordinate axis Ax intersects the line (7.1) at the isolated point A (0, 0) and at the point B (-1, 0).

The asymptotes (7.4 : 1) and (7.4 : 2) of the indicatrix (7.1) (which are nonparallel to the Ax^1 or Ax^2 axis) harmonically separate the Ax^1 and Ax^2 axes of the canonical frame.

The equation of the indicatrix (6.9) corresponding to a point A of the hyperbolic type ($\alpha = -1$) is:

$$x^1 (3x^{2^2} + x^{1^2}) = x^{2^2} - x^{1^2}. \qquad (7.5)$$

This line intersects the Ax^1 axis at the points A (0, 0) and B (-1, 0) and has an asymptote given by the equation

$$x^1 = \frac{1}{3}. \qquad (7.6)$$

The line (7.5) is shown in Figure 2.

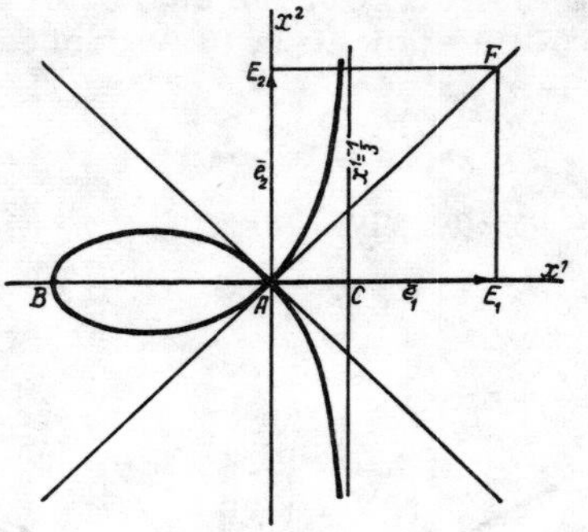

FIGURE 2

From equation (7.5):

$$\frac{x^2}{x^1} = \pm\sqrt{\frac{1+x^1}{1-3x^1}}\,. \tag{7.7}$$

Consequently, the equations of the tangents to the branches of this line at the point A are:

$$x^2 = x^1; \tag{7.8}$$

$$x^2 = -x^1. \tag{7.9}$$

The tangents to the branches of the indicatrix (7.5) at the point A harmonically separate the Ax^1 and Ax^2 axes of the canonical frame.

§ 8. Geometric interpretation of the choice of the axes of the canonical frame. It was stated in § 3 that the Ax^3 axis of the canonical frame $(A, \bar{e}_1, \bar{e}_2, \bar{e}_3)$ is a straight line containing the centers of the osculating Darboux quadrics. To point A of the elliptic type corresponds the indicatrix (7.1) with three asymptotes (7.4) of which only one does not pass through A. The Ax^2 axis is parallel to this asymptote. The Ax^1 axis is conjugate to the Ax^2 axis relative to the surface (A) and the point A.

Indeed, for the choice of values (8.1) Chapter V, the condition of conjugation of the vectors (4.10) Chapter V is:

$$\alpha \underset{1}{\omega^1} \underset{2}{\omega^1} + \underset{1}{\omega^2} \underset{2}{\omega^2} = 0.$$

Therefore the vectors

$$d_1\bar{A} = \underset{1}{\omega^1}\bar{e}_1; \quad d_2\bar{A} = \underset{2}{\omega^2}\bar{e}_2$$

are conjugate.

To point A of the hyperbolic type corresponds the indicatrix (7.5) with the single asymptote (7.6). The Ax^2 axis is parallel to this asymptote; the Ax^1 axis is conjugate to the Ax^2 axis.

§ 9. Geometric interpretation of the choice of coordinate vectors. At a point of the elliptic type the Ax^1 axis (see Figure 1) intersects the indicatrix (7.1) at the point $B(-1, 0)$ on the plane x^1Ax^2.

This defines the unit point E_1 on the Ax^1 axis, symmetric to the point B with respect to the origin A.

Furthermore, the asymptote (7.4 : 3) intersects the Ax^1 axis at the point $C\left(\frac{1}{3}, 0\right)$. This again defines the point E_1. If we draw a straight line through the point E_1 parallel to Ax^2, then, from equations (7.1), it will intersect the given indicatrix at the points $F(1, 1)$ and $G(1, -1)$. This defines the unit point E_2 on the Ax^2 axis. Now, in addition to the unit vectors $\overline{e_1}=\overline{AE_1}$ and $\overline{e_2}=\overline{AE_2}$, we can give the geometric interpretation of the choice of the third coordinate vector $\overline{e_3}=\overline{AE_3}$ on the Ax^3 axis.

If we draw a straight line parallel to the affine normal Ax^3 through the point F, then at its intersection with the osculating paraboloid (1.2), the equation of which is now

$$2x^3 = {x^1}^2 + {x^2}^2, \tag{9.1}$$

we obtain the point $H(1, 1, 1)$. We obtain the point E_3 at the intersection between the Ax^3 axis and the plane passing through the point H parallel to the plane x^1Ax^2.

The Ax^1 axis (see Figure 2) intersects the line (7.5) (for a point A of the hyperbolic type) at the points $A(0, 0)$, $B(-1, 0)$ and the asymptote (7.6) at the point $C\left(\frac{1}{3}, 0\right)$.

The unit point E_1 on the Ax^1 axis is symmetric to the point B with respect to the origin A. This defines the coordinate vector $\overline{e_1}=\overline{AE_1}$.

At the intersection of the tangent (7.8) to the single branch of the line (7.5) and the straight line passing through the point E_1 parallel to the Ax^2 axis lies the point $F(1, 1)$. Therefore the unit point E_2 on the Ax^2 axis lies also on the straight line passing through the point F parallel to the Ax^1 axis. We have obtained the geometric interpretation of the choice of the coordinate vector $\overline{e_2}=\overline{AE_2}$. The equation of the osculating paraboloid (1.2) corresponding to the point under consideration is:

$$2x^3 = {x^2}^2 - {x^1}^2. \tag{9.2}$$

The straight line which passes through the point E_2 and is parallel to the normal Ax^3 intersects the paraboloid (9.2) at the point $D(0, 1, 1/2)$. Let us construct a point H on the straight line E_2D such that

$$E_2D = DH.$$

The coordinates of the point H are $(0, 1, 1)$. The unit point E_3 on the Ax^3 axis also lies on the plane passing through the point H parallel to the plane x^1Ax^2.

Chapter VII

GEOMETRIC INTERPRETATION OF DIFFERENTIAL INVARIANTS

§ 1. Displacement of a point along the line ω^1. For the displacement of a point A along the line ω^1 the form is

$$\omega^2 = 0. \tag{1.1}$$

Consequently, equations (9.1–9.2) of Chapter V become

$$D\omega^1 \big|_{\omega^2=0} = 0;\ \omega^1 \big|_{\omega^2=0} = ds^1; \tag{1.2}$$

$$\frac{d\overline{A}}{ds^1} = \overline{e}_1. \tag{1.3}$$

Let us obtain the infinitesimal displacements of the unit points E_1, E_2, E_3 of the canonical frame $(A, \overline{e}_1, \overline{e}_2, \overline{e}_3)$. The radius vectors of the unit points relative to the origin of any fixed frame are respectively $\overline{A}+\overline{e}_1$, $\overline{A}+\overline{e}_2$, $\overline{A}+\overline{e}_3$. We have

$$d(\overline{A}+\overline{e}_1)_{\omega^2=0} = (d\overline{A} + \omega_1^i \overline{e}_i)_{\omega^2=0}.$$

Replacing the forms ω_1^i by their expressions in the system (9.1) of Chapter V and using the conditions (1.1–1.3), we obtain

$$\frac{d(\overline{A}+\overline{e}_1)}{ds^1} = \left(q_1 + \frac{1}{2}\right)\overline{e}_1 - \frac{2p_2 + aq_2}{3}\overline{e}_2 + a\,\overline{e}_3. \tag{1.4}$$

The invariants $q_1 + \frac{1}{2}$, $-\frac{2p_2 + aq_2}{3}$, are the coordinates of the displacement vector (1.4) of the unit point E_1 of the canonical frame for displacement of the point A along the line ω^1.

The projection of the vector (1.4) onto the normal Ax^3 parallel to the tangent plane x^1Ax^2 is a.

In the same way we obtain

$$\frac{d(\overline{A}+\overline{e}_2)}{ds^1} = \left(1 + \frac{2ap_2 + q_2}{3}\right)\overline{e}_1 + \left(q_1 + \frac{1}{2}\right)\overline{e}_2; \tag{1.5}$$

$$\frac{d(\overline{A}+\overline{e}_3)}{ds^1} = \left(1 + \frac{a}{2} + p_1\right)\overline{e}_1 + ap_2\overline{e}_2 + 2q_1\overline{e}_3. \tag{1.6}$$

The line described by the unit point E_2 of the canonical frame $(A, \overline{e}_1, \overline{e}_2, \overline{e}_3)$ for displacement of the point A along the line ω^1 osculates with the tangent plane x^1Ax^2. The invariants $1 + \frac{2ap_2 + q_2}{3}$, $q_1 + \frac{1}{2}$ are the first and second coordinates of the displacement vector (1.5) of the unit point E_2.

The invariants $1 + \frac{a}{2} + p_1$, ap_2, $2q_1$ are the coordinates of the displacement vector (1.6) of the unit point E_3 for motion of the point A along the line ω^1.

§ 2. Displacement of a point along the line ω^2. For the displacement of a point A along the line ω^2, the form is

$$\omega^1 = 0. \tag{2.1}$$

Consequently, (9.1–9.2) of Chapter V become:

$$D\omega^2\big|_{\omega^1=0}=0;\quad \omega^2\big|_{\omega^1=0}=ds^2; \tag{2.2}$$

$$\frac{d\bar{A}}{ds^2}=\bar{e}_2. \tag{2.3}$$

Differentiating the vectors $\bar{A}+\bar{e}_1$, $\bar{A}+\bar{e}_2$, $\bar{A}+\bar{e}_3$, using the conditions (2.1–2.3). and replacing the forms ω_i^j by their expressions in the system (2.1) of Chapter V, we obtain

$$\frac{d(\bar{A}+\bar{e}_1)}{ds^2}=q_2\bar{e}_1+\left(\frac{3}{2}+\frac{q_1-ap_1+ap_3}{3}\right)\bar{e}_2; \tag{2.4}$$

$$\frac{d(\bar{A}+\bar{e}_2)}{ds^2}=\left(\frac{a}{2}-\frac{aq_1-p_1+p_3}{3}\right)\bar{e}_1+(q_2+1)\bar{e}_2+\bar{e}_3; \tag{2.5}$$

$$\frac{d(\bar{A}+\bar{e}_3)}{ds^2}=p_2\bar{e}_1+\left(1+\frac{a}{2}+p_3\right)\bar{e}_2+2q_2\bar{e}_3. \tag{2.6}$$

The line described by the unit point E_1 of the canonical frame $(A, \bar{e}_1, \bar{e}_2, \bar{e}_3)$ for displacement of the point A along the line ω^2 osculates with the tangent plane x^1Ax^2. The invariants q_2, $\frac{3}{2}+\frac{q_1-ap_1+ap_3}{3}$ are the first and second coordinates of the displacement vector (2.4) of the unit point E_1 for motion of the point A along the line ω^2.

The invariants $\frac{a}{2}-\frac{aq_1-p_1+p_3}{3}$, q_2+1 are the first and second coordinates of the displacement vector (2.5) of the unit point E_2 for motion of the point A along the line ω^2.

The projection of the vector (2.5) on the normal Ax^3 parallel to the tangent plane x^1Ax^2 equals unity.

The invariants p_2, $1+\frac{a}{2}+p_3$, $2q_2$ are the coordinates of the displacement vector (2.6) of the unit point E_3 for motion of the point A along the line ω^2.

§ 3. Tangents to the coordinate lines of one family at points of the coordinate line of another family. Let

$$\bar{P}_1=\bar{A}+t\bar{e}_1 \tag{3.1}$$

be the radius vector of the point P_1 on the tangent to the line ω^1 at the point A with reference to a certain fixed frame. For displacement of the point A along the line ω^2 we obtain

$$d\bar{P}_1\big|_{\omega^1=0}=(dt+tq_2\omega^2)\bar{e}_1+\omega^2\left[1+t\left(\frac{1}{2}+\frac{q_1-ap_1+ap_3}{3}\right)\right]\bar{e}_2.$$

On the Ax^1 axis there exists a point P_1 corresponding to the value

$$t=\frac{-1}{\frac{1}{2}+\frac{q_1-ap_1+ap_3}{3}}. \tag{3.2}$$

For motion of the point A along the line ω^2, this point describes an edge of regression of the surface formed by the tangents to the coordinate line ω^1 at points of the line ω^2. If

$$\bar{P}_2=\bar{A}+t\bar{e}_2$$

is the radius vector of the point P_2 on the tangent to the line ω^2 at the point A, then in the same way we obtain

$$d\overline{P}_2 = \omega^1 \left(1 + t\,\frac{2ap_2 + q_2}{3}\right) \overline{e}_1 + \left[dt + t\left(q_1 + \frac{1}{2}\right)\right] \overline{e}_2.$$

On the Ax^2 axis there is a point P_2 corresponding to the value

$$t = \frac{-3}{2ap_2 + q_2}. \tag{3.3}$$

This point describes the edge of regression of the developable surface formed by the tangents to the coordinate lines ω^2 at the points of the line ω^1 when the point A describes the line ω^1.

Chapter VIII

CERTAIN LINES ON THE SURFACE

§ 1. Conjugate directions. Asymptotic lines. The two vectors

$$d_1\overline{A} = \underset{1}{\omega^1}\overline{e}_1 + \underset{1}{\omega^2}\overline{e}_2; \quad d_2\overline{A} = \underset{2}{\omega^1}\overline{e}_1 + \underset{2}{\omega^2}\overline{e}_2,$$

are conjugate with respect to the surface (A) and the point A if, in conformity with equation (4.10) of Chapter V and the conditions (8.1) of Chapter V,

$$a\underset{1}{\omega^1}\underset{2}{\omega^1} + \underset{1}{\omega^2}\underset{2}{\omega^2} = 0. \tag{1.1}$$

Consequently, the coordinates ω^1, ω^2 of the vector $d\overline{A}$ with the asymptotic direction satisfy the equation

$$a{\omega^1}^2 + {\omega^2}^2 = 0. \tag{1.2}$$

Asymptotic lines on a surface consisting of points of the hyperbolic type are real, while those on a surface consisting of points of the elliptic type are imaginary.

§ 2. Straight lines. If there exists a straight line on the surface, then for displacement along it of the point A

$$d^2\overline{A} = \lambda d\overline{A}.$$

Replacing $d\overline{A}$ and $d^2\overline{A}$ in the above according to formulas (10.2) of Chapter V and eliminating λ, we obtain

$$\begin{aligned} \omega^2 d\omega^1 - \omega^1 d\omega^2 + \frac{1}{3}(2p_2 + aq_2)\,{\omega^1}^3 + \left[\frac{a}{3}(p_1 - p_3) - \right.\\ \left. - \frac{1}{3}q_1 - \frac{3}{2}\right]{\omega^1}^2\omega^2 + \left(\frac{2a}{3}p_2 + \frac{1}{3}q_2\right)\omega^1{\omega^2}^2 + \\ + \left(\frac{a}{2} - \frac{aq_1 - p_1 + p_3}{3}\right){\omega^2}^3 = 0; \end{aligned} \tag{2.1}$$

$$a{\omega^1}^2 + {\omega^2}^2 = 0.$$

Consequently, a straight line on the surface is an asymptotic line of this surface and, for $a = -1$, is given by

$$\omega^2 = \pm\,\omega^1, \tag{2.2}$$

while for $a=+1$ it is given by

$$\omega^2 = \pm i\omega^1 \quad (i=\sqrt{-1}). \tag{2.3}$$

But the requirements (2.2) or (2.3) are not consistent with equation (2.1 : 1), as can be shown, say, by replacing the form ω^2 in the above by its expression in equations (2.2) and (2.3).

This means that the origin of the chosen frame cannot be taken at a point belonging to a straight line on the surface or, therefore, to a ruled surface.

§ 3. Plane lines. The condition that the line described by the point A on the surface (A) be plane is:

$$|d\overline{A}\, d^2\overline{A}\ d^3\overline{A}| = 0. \tag{3.1}$$

We have

$$\left.\begin{aligned} d\overline{A} &= \omega^\alpha\, \overline{e}_\alpha; \\ d^2\overline{A} &= \left(d\omega^\alpha + \omega^\beta \omega_\beta^\alpha\right)\overline{e}_\alpha + \omega^\beta \omega_\beta^3 \overline{e}_3; \\ d^3\overline{A} &= \left[d\left(d\omega^\alpha + \omega^\beta\omega_\beta^\alpha\right) + \left(d\omega^\gamma + \omega^\beta\omega_\beta^\gamma\right)\omega_\gamma^\alpha + \omega^\beta\omega_\beta^3\omega_3^\alpha\right]\overline{e}_\alpha + \\ &\quad + \left[\left(d\omega^\alpha + \omega^\beta\omega_\beta^\alpha\right)\omega_\alpha^3 + d\omega^\beta\omega_\beta^3 + \omega^\beta\omega_\beta^3\omega_3^3\right]\overline{e}_3 \\ &\qquad (\alpha,\ \beta,\ \gamma = 1, 2). \end{aligned}\right\} \tag{3.2}$$

Replacing $d\overline{A}$, $d^2\overline{A}$, $d^3\overline{A}$ by their expressions (3.2) in the condition (3.1), we obtain the differential equation for plane lines on the surface (A) in the form

$$\begin{vmatrix} \omega^1, & d\omega^1 + \omega^\beta\omega_\beta^1, & d\left(d\omega^1 + \omega^\beta\omega_\beta^1\right) + \left(d\omega^\gamma + \omega^\beta\omega_\beta^\gamma\right)\omega_\gamma^1 + \omega^\beta\omega_\beta^3\omega_3^1 \\ \omega^2, & d\omega^2 + \omega^\beta\omega_\beta^2, & d\left(d\omega^2 + \omega^\beta\omega_\beta^2\right) + \left(d\omega^\gamma + \omega^\beta\omega_\beta^\gamma\right)\omega_\gamma^2 + \omega^\beta\omega_\beta^3\omega_3^2 \\ 0 & \omega^\beta\omega_\beta^3, & \left(d\omega^\alpha + \omega^\beta\omega_\beta^\alpha\right)\omega_\alpha^3 + d\omega^\beta\omega_\beta^3 + \omega^\beta\omega_\beta^3\omega_3^3 \end{vmatrix} = 0. \tag{3.3}$$

If the canonical frame $(A, \overline{e}_1, \overline{e}_2, \overline{e}_3)$ chosen in Chapter V moves together with the point A, then the forms ω_i^j $(i, j=1, 2, 3)$ should be replaced in equation (3.3) by their expressions in equations (9.1) of Chapter V.

Every plane line passing through the point A is distinguished by the initial conditions $(d\overline{A})_0$, $(d^2\overline{A})_0$, $(d^3\overline{A})_0$ corresponding to this point

$$|\,d\overline{A}\ \ d^2\overline{A}\ \ d^3\overline{A}\,|_0 = 0,$$

as an integral curve which is a particular solution of equation (3.3).

§ 4. Lines with osculating planes normal to the surface. If

$$d\overline{A} = \omega^1\overline{e}_1 + \omega^2\,\overline{e}_2 \tag{4.1}$$

is the vector tangent to the line on the surface (A) at the point A, then equation (10.2) of Chapter V is

$$\begin{aligned} d^2\overline{A} &= \left[d\omega^1 + \left(q_1 - \frac{1}{2}\right){\omega^1}^2 + \frac{2}{3}\left(a p_2 + 2q_2\right)\omega^1\omega^2 + \right. \\ &\quad \left. + \left(\frac{a}{2} - \frac{a q_1 - p_1 + p_3}{3}\right){\omega^2}^2\right]\overline{e}_1 + \left[d\omega^2 + \frac{1}{3}\left(2p_2 + a q_2\right){\omega^1}^2 + \right. \\ &\quad \left. + \left(1 + \frac{4q_1 - a p_1 + a p_3}{3}\right)\omega^1\omega^2 + q_2{\omega^2}^2\right]\overline{e}_2 + \left(a{\omega^1}^2 + {\omega^2}^2\right)\overline{e}_3. \end{aligned} \tag{4.2}$$

The condition that the osculating plane of this line at the point A pass through the normal to the surface is

$$|\bar{e}_3 \; d\bar{A} \; d^2\bar{A}| = 0.$$

Replacing $d\bar{A}$ and $d^2\bar{A}$ in the above by their expressions in (4.1–4.2), we obtain the differential equation of lines on the surface (A) the osculating planes of which pass through the normals to the surface at the points of contact

$$\omega^2 \left[d\omega^1 + \left(q_1 - \frac{1}{2}\right){\omega^1}^2 + \frac{2}{3}(\alpha p_2 + 2q_2)\,\omega^1\omega^2 + \right.$$
$$\left. + \left(\frac{\alpha}{2} - \frac{\alpha q_1 - p_1 + p_3}{3}\right){\omega^2}^2\right] - \omega^1\left[d\omega^2 - \frac{1}{3}(2p_2 + \alpha q_2)\,{\omega^1}^2 + \right.$$
$$\left. + \left(1 + \frac{4q_1 - \alpha p_1 + \alpha p_3}{3}\right)\omega^1\omega^2 + q_2{\omega^2}^2\right] = 0. \tag{4.3}$$

§ 5. Displacement of a point belonging to the normal. For the displacement (4.1) of the point A, we obtain the infinitesimal displacement of the point P on the normal the radius vector of which is $\bar{P} = \bar{A} + \lambda\bar{e}_3$ in the form

$$d(\bar{A} + \lambda\bar{e}_3) = \left(\omega^1 + \lambda\omega_3^1\right)\bar{e}_1 + \left(\omega^2 + \lambda\omega_3^2\right)\bar{e}_2 + \left(d\lambda + \lambda\omega_3^3\right)\bar{e}_3. \tag{5.1}$$

If the displacement vector of the point P is coplanar with the vectors $\bar{e}_3$ and $d\bar{A}$, then

$$\omega_3^1 : \omega^1 = \omega_3^2 : \omega^2, \tag{5.2}$$

independently of the value of λ. Replacing the forms ω_3^1, ω_3^2 in the above by their expressions in (9.1) of Chapter V, we obtain

$$\alpha p_2{\omega^1}^2 + (p_3 - p_1)\,\omega^1\omega^2 - p_2{\omega^2}^2 = 0. \tag{5.3}$$

Consequently, if the direction of the vector $d\bar{A}$, which is tangent at the point A to a line on the surface satisfies the condition (5.3), then the normals to the surface on this line form a developable surface and the normal plane $A\bar{e}_3 d\bar{A}$ is the tangent plane to this surface.

Equation (5.3) in $\omega^1{:}\omega^2$ has two real solutions, two conjugate complex solutions, one solution or goes over to an identity, according as

$$(p_1 - p_3)^2 + 4\alpha p_2^2 > 0; \tag{5.4}$$
$$(p_1 - p_3)^2 + 4\alpha p_2^2 < 0; \tag{5.5}$$
$$(p_1 - p_3)^2 + 4\alpha p_2^2 = 0; \tag{5.6}$$

or

$$p_1 = p_3, \; p_2 = 0. \tag{5.7}$$

It follows from the condition (5.4) that through a point of the elliptic type there pass two (real) tangential straight lines tangent to those lines on which the normals to the surface (A) constitute a developable surface; through a point of the hyperbolic type there pass two such straight lines when

$$(p_1 - p_3)^2 > 4p_2^2. \tag{5.8}$$

The conditions (5.5–5.6) are applicable only to points of the hyperbolic type. For the conditions (5.7), the normals to the surface at points belonging to any line passing through A constitute a developable surface.

§ 6. Lines of curvature. By line of curvature on the surface is meant a line on which the normals to the surface constitute a developable surface. Let the normals to the surface on a line of curvature form a developable surface with an edge of regression osculating with the normal Ax^3 at the point P. The radius vector of the point P relative to a certain frame is

$$\overline{P} = \overline{A} + \lambda \overline{e}_3.$$

For infinitesimal displacement of the point A along the indicated line, there is a corresponding infinitesimal displacement of the point P collinear with the vector $\overline{e}_3$

$$d(\overline{A} + \lambda \overline{e}_3) = (d\lambda + \lambda\omega_3^3)\,\overline{e}_3,$$

with

$$\omega^1 + \lambda\omega_3^1 = 0; \quad \omega^2 + \lambda\omega_3^2 = 0. \tag{6.1}$$

The condition of compatibility of these equations is relatively identical with the condition (5.3). Consequently, on a surface consisting of points of the elliptic type there exist two families of (real) lines of curvature; on a surface consisting of points of the hyperbolic type there are two or one family of lines of curvature according as the condition (5.4) or (5.5) is fulfilled; for the conditions (5.7), every line on the surface is a line of curvature.

The points F_1 and F_2 with radius vectors

$$\overline{F}_\alpha = \overline{A} + \lambda_\alpha \overline{e}_3 \quad (\alpha = 1, 2)$$

are called the foci of the normal Ax^3 of the surface (A) if λ_1 and λ_2, the values of λ in equations (6.1) corresponding to the given $\omega^1{:}\omega^2$, are roots of equation (5.3). Otherwise the focus of the normal to the surface (A) is a point – the edge of regression of the developable surface formed by the normals to the surface (A).

The surfaces (F_1) and (F_2) formed by the foci of the normals of the surface (A) are called the focal surfaces of congruence of these normals.

§ 7. Normal sections of the surface. If the line l on the surface is specified by equations (5.2) of Chapter VII, then the equations for infinitesimal displacements of the canonical frame of the surface for motion of the point A along this line assume the form (5.4) of Chapter VI. Let

$$\frac{d\overline{A}}{d\sigma} = \lambda^1 \overline{e}_1 + \lambda^2 \overline{e}_2 = \overline{u}_1, \tag{7.1}$$

the vector of infinitesimal displacement of the point A which describes the line l, be the normal section of the surface (A) by the plane $\left(A\, \overline{e}_3\, \frac{d\overline{A}}{d\sigma}\right)$.

For motion of the point A of this line, the vector $\overline{u}_1$ remains in the indicated normal plane but the vector $\overline{e}_3$ does not in general belong to this surface.

The conditions (5.7) of Chapter VI are, corresponding to the point A,

$$\frac{d\lambda^\alpha}{d\sigma} + \lambda^\beta \lambda_\beta^\alpha = \varphi\lambda^\alpha \quad (\alpha, \beta, \gamma = 1, 2) \tag{7.2}$$

and

$$\frac{d^2\overline{A}}{d\sigma^2} = \varphi\lambda^\alpha \overline{e}_\alpha + \lambda^\beta \lambda_\beta^3 \overline{e}_3. \tag{7.3}$$

Let $(A, \overline{u}_1, \overline{u}_2)$ be the canonical frame referred to the line l and the point A.

The equations for its infinitesimal displacements (5.2, Introduction) are

$$\frac{d\overline{A}}{d\sigma} = \overline{u}_1; \quad \frac{d\overline{u}_1}{d\sigma} = k\overline{u}_1 + \overline{u}_2; \quad \frac{d\overline{u}_2}{d\sigma} = \varepsilon\overline{u}_1 + 2k\overline{u}_2. \tag{7.4}$$

Consequently

$$\overline{u}_2 = (\varphi - k)\,\overline{u}_1 + \lambda^{\beta}\lambda^{3}_{\beta}\overline{e}_3; \tag{7.5}$$

$$\frac{d^3\overline{A}}{d\sigma^3} = \left[\frac{d}{d\sigma}\left(\frac{d\lambda^{\alpha}}{d\sigma} + \lambda^{\beta}\lambda^{\alpha}_{\beta}\right) + \varphi\lambda^{\gamma}\lambda^{\alpha}_{\gamma} + \lambda^{\beta}\lambda^{3}_{\beta}\lambda^{\alpha}_{3}\right]\overline{e}_{\alpha} +$$
$$+ \left[\frac{d\,(\lambda^{\beta}\lambda^{3}_{\beta})}{d\sigma} + \left(\varphi + \lambda^{3}_{3}\right)\lambda^{\beta}\lambda^{3}_{\beta}\right]\overline{e}_3. \tag{7.6}$$

For the conditions (7.1–7.3), (7.6) equation (3.3) may be replaced by the system

$$\frac{d}{d\sigma}\left(\frac{d\lambda^{\alpha}}{d\sigma} + \lambda^{\beta}\lambda^{\alpha}_{\beta}\right) + \varphi\lambda^{\beta}\lambda^{\alpha}_{\beta} + \lambda^{\beta}\lambda^{3}_{\beta}\lambda^{\alpha}_{3} = \psi\lambda^{\alpha}. \tag{7.7}$$

From equations (7.6), (7.7), (7.4–7.5) we have

$$\psi = \frac{dk}{d\sigma} - 2k^2 + 3k\varphi + \varepsilon; \tag{7.8}$$

$$\varphi = 3k - \lambda^{3}_{3} - \frac{1}{\lambda^{\beta}\lambda^{3}_{\beta}}\,\frac{d\,(\lambda^{\beta}\lambda^{3}_{\beta})}{d\sigma}. \tag{7.9}$$

Replacing $\frac{d\lambda^{\alpha}}{d\sigma}$ by (7.2) in the expression for the derivative $\frac{d\,(\lambda^{\beta}\lambda^{3}_{\beta})}{d\sigma}$ and $\lambda^{3}_{1}, \lambda^{3}_{2}, \lambda^{2}_{1}, \lambda^{1}_{2}$ by (5.4), Chapter VI, we obtain

$$\frac{d\,(\lambda^{\beta}\lambda^{3}_{\beta})}{d\sigma} = 2\left[\varphi\left(\lambda\lambda^{1^2} + \lambda^{2^2}\right) - a\lambda^{1}_{1}\lambda^{1^2} - \lambda^{1}\lambda^{2^2} - \lambda^{2}_{2}\lambda^{2^2}\right]. \tag{7.10}$$

Now, replacing $\lambda^{1}_{1}, \lambda^{2}_{2}$ by their expressions in (5.4), Chapter VI, equation (7.9) can be written in the form

$$\varphi = k - \frac{\lambda^{3}_{3}}{3} + 2\,\frac{\left(aq_1 - \frac{a}{2}\right)\lambda^{1^3} + aq_2\lambda^{1^2}\lambda^{2} + \left(q_1 + \frac{3}{2}\right)\lambda^{1}\lambda^{2^2} + q_2\lambda^{2^3}}{3\left(a\lambda^{1^2} + \lambda^{2^2}\right)}. \tag{7.11}$$

From equations (7.5), (7.11) and equation (5.4) of Chapter VI it follows that

$$\overline{u}_2 = \frac{\lambda^{1}\left(3\lambda^{2^2} - a\lambda^{1^2}\right)}{3\left(a\lambda^{1^2} + \lambda^{2^2}\right)}\,\overline{u}_1 + \left(a\lambda^{1^2} + \lambda^{2^2}\right)\overline{e}_3. \tag{7.12}$$

It follows from the above that: the normal to the normal section of the surface *(A)* at the point *A* coincides with the normal to the surface *(A)* at the point *A* if

$$\lambda^{1}\left(3\lambda^{2^2} - a\lambda^{1^2}\right) = 0. \tag{7.13}$$

There are three such directions: they are all real if the point *A* is of the hyperbolic type; however, if the point is of the elliptic type, then one direction, Ax^2, is real and the remaining two are conjugate complex. It follows from (7.12) that the equations of the normal to the normal section at the point A in the frame $(A, \bar{e}_1, \bar{e}_2, \bar{e}_3)$ are

$$\frac{x^1}{\lambda^{1^2}(3\lambda^{2^2}-\alpha\lambda^{1^2})}=\frac{x^2}{\lambda^1\lambda^2(3\lambda^{2^2}-\alpha\lambda^{1^2})}=\frac{x^3}{3(\alpha\lambda^{1^2}+\lambda^{2^2})^2} \qquad (7.14)$$

Eliminating the ratio $\lambda^1:\lambda^2$ from the above, we obtain the equation of a cone of normals to the normal section of the surface (A) at the point A in the form

$$3(\alpha x^{1^2}+x^{2^2})^2=x^1x^3(3x^{2^2}-\alpha x^{1^2}). \qquad (7.15)$$

The normals to the normal sections of the surface (A) at the point A form a cone of the fourth order.

If we cut this cone by a plane the equation of which in the frame $(A, \bar{e}_1, \bar{e}_2, \bar{e}_3)$ is

$$x^3=1, \qquad (7.16)$$

then the equation of the projection of the obtained directrix of the cone onto the plane Ax^1x^2 parallel to the normal Ax^3 is

$$3(\alpha x^{1^2}+x^{2^2})=x^1(3x^{2^2}-\alpha x^{1^2}). \qquad (7.17)$$

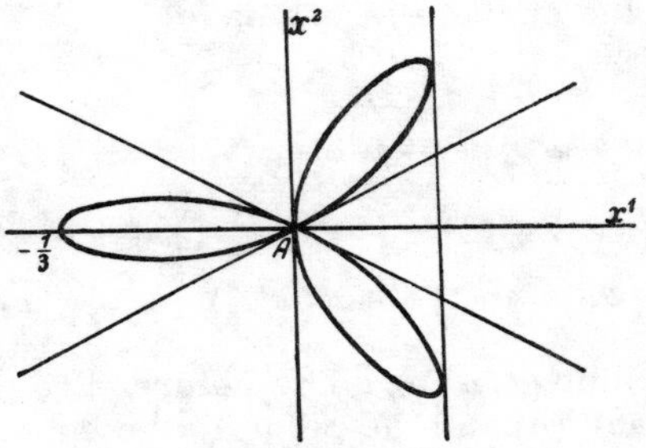

FIGURE 3

To a point of the elliptic type corresponds the line shown in Figure 3, to a point of hyperbolic type the line shown in Figure 4. The tangents to the branches of the line (7.17) at the point A are for $\alpha = 1$:

$$x^1=0; \qquad (7.18)$$

$$x^2=\frac{1}{\sqrt{3}}x^1; \qquad (7.19)$$

$$x^2=-\frac{1}{\sqrt{3}}x^1. \qquad (7.20)$$

The asymptotes of the line (7.17) for $\alpha = -1$ have asymptotic directions with respect to the surface (A) and the point A; their equations are

$$x^2=x^1; \qquad (7.21)$$

$$x^2=-x^1 \qquad (7.22)$$

It also follows from formula (7.12) that the corresponding normal sections of the surface have no affine normal. The Ax^2 axis osculates with the line (7.17) at the point A.

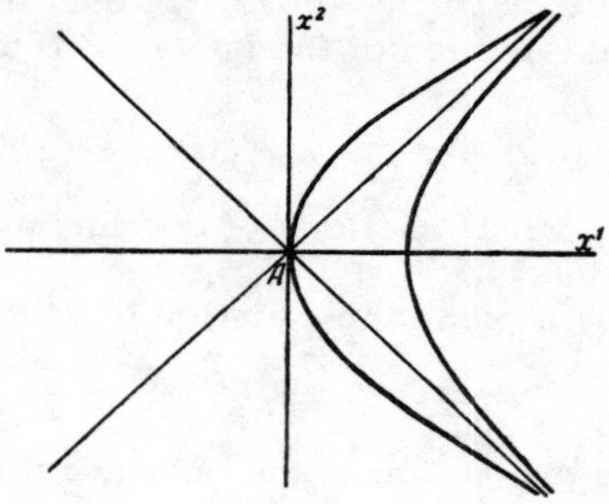

FIGURE 4

§ 8. **Lines having normal planes normal to the surface.** For displacement of the point A on the surface (A) we have:

$$\left.\begin{aligned} &d\bar{A} = \omega^{\alpha}\bar{e}_{\alpha} \quad (\alpha, \beta, \gamma = 1, 2);\\ &d^2\bar{A} = \left(d\omega^{\alpha} + \omega^{\beta}\omega^{\alpha}_{\beta}\right)\bar{e}_{\alpha} + \omega^{\beta}\omega^{3}_{\beta}\bar{e}_3;\\ &d^3\bar{A} = \left[d\left(d\omega^{\alpha} + \omega^{\beta}\omega^{\alpha}_{\beta}\right) + \left(d\omega^{\beta} + \omega^{\gamma}\omega^{\beta}_{\lambda}\right)\omega^{\alpha}_{\beta} + \omega^{\beta}\omega^{3}_{\beta}\omega^{\alpha}_{3}\right]\bar{e}_{\alpha} + \\ &\qquad + \left[\left(d\omega^{\alpha} + \omega^{\beta}\omega^{\alpha}_{\beta}\right)\omega^{3}_{\alpha} + d\left(\omega^{\beta}\omega^{3}_{\beta}\right) + \omega^{\beta}\omega^{3}_{\beta}\omega^{3}_{3}\right]\bar{e}_3. \end{aligned}\right\} \tag{8.1}$$

Let the canonical frame $(A, \bar{u}_1, \bar{u}_2, \bar{u}_3)$ be referred to the line described by the point A on the surface (A) and the point A; the equations for infinitesimal displacements of this frame are (5.2, Chapter III)

$$\frac{d\bar{A}}{d\sigma} = \bar{u}_1; \quad \frac{d\bar{u}_1}{d\sigma} = k_1 u_1 + \bar{u}_2; \quad \frac{d\bar{u}_2}{d\sigma} = \varepsilon\bar{u}_1 + 2k_1\bar{u}_2 + \bar{u}_3; \quad \frac{d\bar{u}_3}{d\sigma} = \\ = k_2\bar{u}_1 + 3\varepsilon\bar{u}_2 + 3k_1\bar{u}_3. \tag{8.2}$$

The condition that the normal plane of this line at the point A pass through the normal to the surface (A) is

$$\lambda\bar{u}_2 + \mu\bar{u}_3 = \nu\bar{e}_3. \tag{8.3}$$

From equations (8.2) and (8.3):

$$\bar{u}_2 = \frac{d^2\bar{A}}{d\sigma^2} - k_1\frac{d\bar{A}}{d\sigma}; \quad \bar{u}_3 = \frac{d^3\bar{A}}{d\sigma^3} - 3k_1\frac{d^2\bar{A}}{d\sigma^2} + \left(2k_1^2 - \varepsilon - \frac{dk_1}{d\sigma}\right)\frac{dA}{d\sigma}; \tag{8.4}$$

$$k_1 = \frac{\left|\frac{d\bar{A}}{d\sigma}\ \frac{d^2\bar{A}}{d\sigma^2}\ \frac{d^4\bar{A}}{d\sigma_4}\right|}{6\left|\frac{d\bar{A}}{d\sigma}\ \frac{d^2\bar{A}}{d\sigma^2}\ \frac{d^3\bar{A}}{d\sigma^3}\right|} = \frac{\frac{d}{a\sigma}\left|\bar{u}_1\bar{u}_2\bar{u}_3\right|}{6\left|\bar{u}\ u_2 u_3\right|}; \tag{8.5}$$

$$\frac{d^4\overline{A}}{d\sigma^4} = \left(\frac{d^2k_1}{d\sigma^2} - 7k_1\frac{dk_1}{d\sigma} + 6k_1{}^3 - 6\varepsilon k_1 + k_2\right)\frac{d\overline{A}}{d\sigma} + \left(4\frac{dk_1}{d\sigma} - \right.$$
$$\left. -11k_1^2 + 4\varepsilon\right)\frac{d^2\overline{A}}{d\sigma^2} + 6k_1\frac{d^3\overline{A}}{d\sigma^3}. \tag{8.6}$$

$$\varepsilon = \frac{35\,|\overline{A^{\rm I}}\,\overline{A^{\rm II}}\,\overline{A^{\rm IV}}\,|^2 - 60\,|\overline{A^{\rm I}}\,\overline{A^{\rm III}}\,\overline{A^{\rm IV}}|\,|\overline{A^{\rm I}}\,\overline{A^{\rm II}}\,\overline{A^{\rm III}}\,|}{144\,|\overline{A^{\rm I}}\,\overline{A^{\rm II}}\,\overline{A^{\rm III}}\,|^2} -$$
$$- \frac{24\,|\overline{A^{\rm I}}\,\overline{A^{\rm II}}\,\overline{A^{\rm III}}|\,|\overline{A^{\rm I}}\,\overline{A^{\rm II}}\,\overline{A^{\rm IV}}|}{144\,|\overline{A^{\rm I}}\,\overline{A^{\rm II}}\,\overline{A^{\rm III}}\,|^2}. \tag{8.7}$$

The primes denote derivatives with respect to σ. Using formulas (8.5), (8.7) and (8.1), the condition (8.3) can be written as a system of two equations

$$\lambda d\sigma\left\{d\omega^\alpha + \omega^\beta\omega_\beta^\alpha - \frac{|d\overline{A}\,d^2\overline{A}\,d^4\overline{A}|}{6\,|d\overline{A}\,d^2\overline{A}\,d^3\overline{A}|}\,\omega\alpha\right\} + \mu\left\{d\left(d\omega^\alpha + \omega^\beta\omega_\beta^\alpha\right) + \right.$$
$$+ \left(d\omega^\beta + \omega^\gamma\omega_\gamma^\beta\right)\omega_\beta^\alpha + \omega^\beta\omega_\beta^3\omega_3^\alpha - \frac{|d\overline{A}\,d^2\overline{A}\,d^4\overline{A}|}{2\,|d\overline{A}\,d^2\overline{A}\,d^3\overline{A}|}\left(d\omega^\alpha + \omega^\beta\omega_\beta^\alpha\right) +$$
$$\left. + \frac{12\,|d\overline{A}\,d^3\overline{A}\,d^4\overline{A}|\cdot|d\overline{A}\,d^2\overline{A}\,d^3\overline{A}| - |d\overline{A}\,d^2\overline{A}\,d^4\overline{A}\,|^2}{48\,|d\overline{A}\,d^2\overline{A}\,d^3\overline{A}\,|^2}\right\}. \tag{8.8}$$

When the forms ω_i^j and the differentials $d\overline{A}, \ldots, d^5\overline{A}$ are replaced by their expressions from (9.1), Chapter V, the above equations become the differential equations of lines on the surface (A) having normal planes which are normal to this surface.

§ 9. Lines having principal normals which coincide with the normals to the surface. If at every point A of a line on the surface (A) the vector of the principal normal $\overline{u}_2$ is collinear with the vector $\overline{e}_3$, then the differential equations of such lines are obtained from (8.8) in the form

$$d\omega^\alpha + \omega^\beta\omega_\beta^\alpha - \frac{|d\overline{A}\,d^2\overline{A}\,d^4\overline{A}|}{6\,|d\overline{A}\,d^2\overline{A}\,d^3\overline{A}|}\,\omega^\alpha = 0. \tag{9.1}$$

Consequently, in order for the principal normals of a line on the surface (in the sense which conforms to the chosen frame) and the first curvature of this line k_1 to be zero at all points of this line, it is necessary and sufficient that these lines be integral lines of the system of equations

$$d\omega^\alpha + \omega^\beta\omega_\beta^\alpha = 0. \tag{9.2}$$

Replacing the forms ω_β^α by their expressions in (9.1), Chapter V, we can write this system of equations in the form

$$\left.\begin{aligned} &d\omega^1 + \omega^1\left[\left(q_1 - \frac{1}{2}\right)\omega^1 + q_2\omega^2\right] + \omega^2\left[\frac{2ap_2 + q_2}{3}\,\omega^1 + \left(\frac{\alpha}{2} - \right.\right. \\ &\qquad \left.\left. - \frac{aq_1 - p_1 + p_3}{3}\right)\omega^2\right] = 0; \\ &d\omega^2 + \omega^1\left[-\frac{2p_2 + aq_2}{3}\,\omega^1 + \left(\frac{1}{2} + \frac{q_1 - ap_1 + ap_3}{3}\right)\omega^2\right] + \\ &\qquad + \omega^2\left[\left(q_1 + \frac{1}{2}\right)\omega^1 + q_2\omega^2\right] = 0. \end{aligned}\right\} \tag{9.3}$$

The lines defined by the above equations have principal normals which coincide with the normals to the surface. In this sense we have an analogue to the geodesic lines on the surface in Euclidean space.

§ 10. Lines having binormals coincident with the normals to the surface. It follows from equations (8.8) that the equations of such lines are:

$$d\left(d\omega^{\alpha}+\omega^{\beta}\omega_{\beta}^{\alpha}\right)+\left(d\omega^{\beta}+\omega^{\gamma}\omega_{\gamma}^{\beta}\right)\omega_{\beta}^{\alpha}+\omega^{\beta}\omega_{\beta}^{3}\omega_{3}^{\alpha}-$$
$$-\frac{|d\bar{A}\,d^{2}\bar{A}\,d^{4}\bar{A}|}{2|d\bar{A}\,d^{2}\bar{A}\,d^{3}\bar{A}|}\left(d\omega^{\alpha}+\omega^{\beta}\omega_{\beta}^{\alpha}\right)+$$
$$+\frac{12|d\bar{A}\,d^{3}\bar{A}\,d^{4}\bar{A}|\,|d\bar{A}\,d^{2}\bar{A}\,d^{3}\bar{A}|-|d\bar{A}\,d^{2}\bar{A}\,d^{4}\bar{A}|^{2}}{48|d\bar{A}\,d^{2}\bar{A}\,d^{3}\bar{A}|^{2}}\omega^{\alpha}=0. \qquad (10.1)$$

The equations of such lines with first curvature k_1 equal to zero are

$$d\left(d\omega^{\alpha}+\omega^{\beta}\omega_{\beta}^{\alpha}\right)+\left(d\omega^{\beta}+\omega^{\gamma}\omega_{\gamma}^{\beta}\right)\omega_{\beta}^{\alpha}+\omega^{\beta}\omega_{\beta}^{3}\omega_{3}^{\alpha}+$$
$$+\frac{|d\bar{A}\,d^{3}\bar{A}\,d^{4}\bar{A}|}{4|d\bar{A}\,d^{2}\bar{A}\,d^{3}\bar{A}|}\omega^{\alpha}=0. \qquad (10.2)$$

In equations (10.1–10.2) the forms ω_{α}^{β} should be replaced by their expressions in equations (9.1) of Chapter V.

§ 11. Lines having rectifying planes normal to the surface. The condition that the rectifying plane of a line on the surface be normal to the surface at this point is:

$$\lambda\bar{u}_1+\mu\bar{u}_3=\nu\bar{e}_3. \qquad (11.1)$$

Replacing u^1, u_3 by their expressions (8.2 : 1) and (8.4 : 2) in the above, we obtain

$$\lambda d\sigma^{2}\omega^{\alpha}+\mu\Big\{d\left(d\omega^{\alpha}+\omega^{\beta}\omega_{\beta}^{\alpha}\right)+\left(d\omega^{\beta}+\omega^{\gamma}\omega_{\gamma}^{\beta}\right)\omega_{\beta}^{\alpha}+\omega^{\beta}\omega_{\beta}^{3}\omega_{3}^{\alpha}-$$
$$-\frac{|d\bar{A}\,d^{2}\bar{A}\,d^{4}\bar{A}|}{2|d\bar{A}\,d^{2}\bar{A}\,d^{3}\bar{A}|}\left(d\omega^{\alpha}+\omega^{\beta}\omega_{\beta}^{\alpha}\right)+$$
$$+\frac{12|d\bar{A}\,d^{3}\bar{A}\,d^{4}\bar{A}|\,|d\bar{A}\,d^{2}\bar{A}\,d^{3}\bar{A}|-|d\bar{A}\,d^{2}\bar{A}\,d^{4}\bar{A}|^{2}}{48|d\bar{A}\,d^{2}\bar{A}\,d^{3}\bar{A}|^{2}}\omega^{\alpha}=0 \qquad (11.2)$$

the differential equations of lines having rectifying planes normal to the surface. The forms ω_{α}^{β} should be replaced by their expressions in equations (9.1) of Chapter V.

Equations (11.2) are for $k_1 = 0$,

$$\lambda\omega^{\alpha}d\sigma^{2}+\mu\Big\{d\left(d\omega^{\alpha}+\omega^{\beta}\omega_{\beta}^{\alpha}\right)+\left(d\omega^{\beta}+\omega^{\gamma}\omega_{\gamma}^{\beta}\right)\omega_{\beta}^{\alpha}+\omega^{\beta}\omega_{\beta}^{3}\omega_{3}^{\alpha}+$$
$$+\frac{|d\bar{A}\,d^{3}\bar{A}\,d^{4}\bar{A}|}{4|d\bar{A}\,d^{2}\bar{A}\,d^{3}\bar{A}|}\omega^{\alpha}=0. \qquad (11.3)$$

Specifying the ratio $\lambda{:}\mu$ in (11.3) and replacing the forms ω_{α}^{β} by their expressions in equations (9.1) of Chapter V, we obtain the differential equations of lines on a surface for which the rectifying planes are normal to the surface and the first curvature $k_1 = 0$.

§ 12. Lines having rectifying planes tangent to the surface. For a line the rectifying plane of which is identical at every point with the tangent plane to the surface, the vector of the binormal $\bar{u}_3$ is coplanar with the vectors $\bar{e}_1$ and $\bar{e}_2$,

$$\bar{u}_3 = \lambda \bar{e}_1 + \mu \bar{e}_2. \tag{12.1}$$

For this condition we obtain from (8.4 : 2) and (8.1)

$$\left(d\omega^\alpha + \omega^\beta \omega_\beta^\alpha\right) \omega_\alpha^3 + \omega^\beta \omega_\beta^3 \omega_3^3 + d\omega^\beta \omega_\beta^3 - \frac{|d\bar{A}\; d^2\bar{A}\; d^4\bar{A}|}{2\,|d\bar{A}\; d^2\bar{A}\; d^3\bar{A}|} \omega^\beta \omega_\beta^3 = 0. \tag{12.2}$$

Replacing the forms ω_α^β and the differentials $d\bar{A}, \ldots, d^4\bar{A}$ in the above by their expressions in equations (9.1), Chapter V, we obtain the differential equation of a line the rectifying plane of which at any point is identical with the tangent plane to the surface.

§ 13. Darboux lines. The equation of osculating quadrics (7.8), Chapter V, under the conditions (8.1), Chapter V, is

$$\alpha x^{1^2} + x^{2^2} - 2x^3 + \frac{b_1}{2} x^1 x^3 + \frac{b_2}{2} x^2 x^3 + A_{33} x^{3^2} = 0. \tag{13.1}$$

At the intersection of any quadric of this three-parameter family and the surface (A) represented by equation (10.6) of Chapter V we obtain a line lying also on a cylindrical surface with generators parallel to the affine normal Ax^3. Eliminating the coordinate x^3 from equation (13.1) and equation (10.6) of Chapter V, we can write the equation of this surface in the form

$$\left(\frac{b_1}{4} - \frac{2}{3}\right) \alpha x^{1^3} + \frac{b_2}{4} \alpha x^{1^2} x^2 + \frac{b_1}{4} x^1 x^{2^2} + \frac{b_2}{4} x^{2^3} + 0\,(4) = 0. \tag{13.2}$$

The above equation can also be regarded as the equation of the projection of the line of intersection of the surface (A) and the quadric (13.1) onto the plane x^1Ax^2 along the normal Ax^3 relative to the Ax^1, Ax^2 axes of the canonical frame $Ax^1x^2x^3$. In general three branches of this line pass through the point A. The conditions that the three branches of the line osculate with each other at the point A are:

$$\left(\frac{b_1}{4} - \frac{2}{3}\right) \alpha x^{1^3} + \frac{b_2}{4} \alpha x^{1^2} x^2 + \frac{b_1}{4} x^1 x^{2^2} + \frac{b_2}{4} x^{2^3} \equiv$$
$$\equiv \left(\frac{b_2}{4} - \frac{2}{3}\right) \alpha (x^1 + t x^2)^3; \tag{13.3}$$

$$\left.\begin{aligned} \frac{b_1}{4} = \left(\frac{b_1}{4} - \frac{2}{3}\right) 3t;\quad \frac{b_1}{4} = \left(\frac{b_1}{4} - \frac{2}{3}\right) \alpha\, 3t^2; \\ \frac{b_2}{4} = \left(\frac{b_1}{4} - \frac{2}{3}\right) \alpha t^3. \end{aligned}\right\} \tag{13.4}$$

Consequently,

$$t^3 - 3\alpha t = 0. \tag{13.5}$$

To a point of the elliptic type ($\alpha = 1$) correspond the following roots of equation (13.5):

$$t_0 = 0;\quad t_1 = \sqrt{3};\quad t_2 = -\sqrt{3}. \tag{13.6}$$

It follows from equations (13.4) that to these roots correspond the following values b_1 and b_2:

$$b_1 = 0;\quad b_2 = 0; \tag{13.7}$$

$$b_1 = 3; \quad b_2 = \sqrt{3}; \tag{13.8}$$

$$b_1 = 3; \quad b_2 = -\sqrt{3}; \tag{13.9}$$

the equations of the quadrics (13.1) are:

$$\alpha x^{1^2} + x^{2^2} - 2x^3 + A_{33}x^{3^2} = 0; \tag{13.10}$$

$$\alpha x^{1^2} + x^{2^2} - 2x^3 + \frac{3}{2}x^1x^3 + \frac{\sqrt{3}}{2}x^2x^3 + A_{33}x^{3^2} = 0; \tag{13.11}$$

$$\alpha x^{1^2} + x^{2^2} - 2x^3 + \frac{3}{2}x^1x^3 - \frac{\sqrt{3}}{2}x^2x^3 + A_{33}x^{3^2} = 0. \tag{13.12}$$

To a point of the hyperbolic type ($\alpha = -1$) correspond the following roots of equation (13.5):

$$t_0 = 0; \quad t_1 = i\sqrt{3}; \quad t_2 = -i\sqrt{3}. \tag{13.13}$$

The direction of the common tangent to the three branches of the line of the family (13.2) at the point A is called the Darboux direction. It follows from the conditions (13.6) and (13.2–13.3) that: a point of the elliptic type is the origin of three Darboux directions; one coincides with the direction of the straight line containing the Ax^2 axis of the canonical frame $(A, \overline{e}_1, \overline{e}_2, \overline{e}_3)$; the other two coincide with the directions of the straight lines

$$x^2 = \frac{1}{\sqrt{3}}x^1; \quad x^2 = -\frac{1}{\sqrt{3}}x^1, \tag{13.14}$$

which harmonically separate the Ax^1 and Ax^2 axes of this frame. A point of the hyperbolic type is the origin of a single real Darboux direction corresponding to the direction of the straight line Ax^2 of the canonical frame $(A, \overline{e}_1, \overline{e}_2, \overline{e}_3)$; the other two directions are conjugate complex.

By a Darboux line is meant a line on the surface at every point of which the tangent has a Darboux direction. On a surface consisting of points of the elliptic type there are three families of real Darboux lines; on a surface consisting of points of the hyperbolic type there is a single family of real Darboux lines and two families of complex Darboux lines. The equations of the indicated (one-parameter) families of lines corresponding to the conditions (13.6) and (13.13) with reference to the chosen canonical frame are:

$$1)\ \omega^1 = 0; \quad 2)\ \omega^1 + \sqrt{3}\,\omega^2 = 0; \quad 3)\ \omega^1 - \sqrt{3}\,\omega^2 = 0. \tag{13.15}$$

$$1)\ \omega^1 = 0; \quad 2)\ \omega^1 + i\sqrt{3}\,\omega^2 = 0; \quad 3)\ \omega^1 - i\sqrt{3}\,\omega^2 = 0. \tag{13.16}$$

It follows from equations (13.15), (13.16) and (7.4–7.6) of Chapter VII that: the (real) Darboux directions at every point on the surface coincide with the directions of the asymptotes of the correspoinding indicatrix of the characteristics of the normal planes. A line on the surface is called a Segrè line if it is conjugate to the lines of the Darboux family. The equations for the families of Segrè lines corresponding to the Darboux lines (13.15) and (13.16) are:

$$1)\ \omega^2 = 0; \quad 2)\ \sqrt{3}\,\omega^1 - \omega^2 = 0; \quad 3)\ \sqrt{3}\,\omega^1 + \omega^2 = 0. \tag{13.17}$$

$$1)\ \omega^2 = 0; \quad 2)\ i\sqrt{3}\,\omega_1 - \omega^2 = 0; \quad 3)\ i\sqrt{3}\,\omega^1 + \omega^2 = 0. \tag{13.18}$$

It follows from equations (13.15–13.18) that: at the points of every line belonging to one of the three Darboux families of lines, the Ax^2 axes of the chosen canonical frames (Chapter V) are tangent to that line; the Ax^1 axes of these frames are tangent at the points of every line belonging to one of the three families of Segrè lines. The Darboux direction coinciding with the direction of the straight line Ax^2 of the canonical frame corresponds to those osculating Darboux quadrics at the point A the centers of which belong to the straight line normal to the surface at this point.

§ 14. Equations for infinitesimal displacements of the chosen frames of the surface and of the line on this surface. The equations (5.4) of Chapter VI are the equations for infinitesimal displacements of the chosen canonical frame of the surface for displacement of the point A over the surface (A). Let $(A, \bar{u}_1, \bar{u}_2, \bar{u}_3)$ be the canonical frame of a line on the surface (A) passing through the point A. The equations for infinitesimal displacements (5.2), Chapter III, of this frame will be:

$$\left.\begin{aligned} &\frac{d\bar{A}}{d\sigma} = \bar{u}_1;\\ &\frac{d\bar{u}_1}{d\sigma} = k_1\bar{u}_1 + \bar{u}_2;\\ &\frac{d\bar{u}_2}{d\sigma} = \varepsilon\bar{u}_1 + 2k_1\bar{u}_2 + \bar{u}_3;\\ &\frac{d\bar{u}_3}{d\sigma} = k_2\bar{u}_1 + 3\varepsilon\bar{u}_2 + 3k_1\bar{u}_3. \end{aligned}\right\} \tag{14.1}$$

We will regard the parameter σ in equations (14.1) and equation (5.4) of Chapter III as identical. Comparing these two systems of equations, one can obtain the relation between the frame of the line $(A, \bar{u}_1, \bar{u}_2, \bar{u}_3)$ to the frame of the surface $(A, \bar{e}_1, \bar{e}_2, \bar{e}_3)$ in the form

$$\left.\begin{aligned} &\bar{u}_1 = \lambda^1\bar{e}_1 + \lambda^2\bar{e}_2;\\ &\bar{u}_2 = a^1\bar{e}_1 + a^2\bar{e}_2 + \left(\alpha\lambda^{1^2} + \lambda^{2^2}\right)\bar{e}_3;\\ &\bar{u}_3 = b^1\bar{e}_1 + b^2\bar{e}_2 + b_3\bar{e}_3, \end{aligned}\right\} \tag{14.2}$$

where

$$\left.\begin{aligned} a^1 = {} & \frac{d\lambda^1}{d\sigma} + \lambda^1\left[\left(q_1 - \frac{1}{2}\right)\lambda^1 + q_2\lambda^2\right] + \lambda^2\left[\frac{2\alpha p_2 + q_2}{3}\lambda^1 + \right.\\ & \left. + \left(\frac{\alpha}{2} - \frac{\alpha q_1 - p_1 + p_3}{3}\right)\lambda^2\right] - k_1\lambda^1;\\ a^2 = {} & \frac{d\lambda^2}{d\sigma} + \lambda^1\left[-\frac{2p_2 + \alpha q_2}{3}\lambda^1 + \left(\frac{1}{2} + \frac{q_1 - \alpha p_1 + \alpha p_3}{3}\right)\lambda^2\right] + \\ & + \lambda^2\left[\left(q_1 + \frac{1}{2}\right)\lambda^1 + q_2\lambda^2\right] - k_1\lambda^2; \end{aligned}\right\} \tag{14.3}$$

$$\left.\begin{aligned} b^1 = {} & \frac{da^1}{d\sigma} + a^1\left[\left(q_1 - \frac{1}{2}\right)\lambda^1 + q_2\lambda^2\right] + a^2\left[\frac{2\alpha p_2 + q_2}{3}\lambda^1 + \right.\\ & \left. + \left(\frac{\alpha}{2} - \frac{\alpha q_1 - p_1 + p_3}{3}\right)\lambda^2\right] + \left(\alpha\lambda^{1^2} + \lambda^{2^2}\right)\left[\left(\frac{\alpha}{2} + p_1\right)\lambda^1 + \right.\\ & \left. + p_2\lambda^2\right] - \varepsilon\lambda^1 - 2k_1a^1; \end{aligned}\right\} \tag{14.4}$$

$$
\left.
\begin{aligned}
b^2 = {} & \frac{da^2}{d\sigma} + a^1\left[-\frac{2p_2+\alpha q_2}{3}\lambda^1 + \left(\frac{1}{2}+\frac{q_1-\alpha p_1+\alpha p_3}{3}\right)\lambda^2\right] + \\
& + a^2\left[\left(q_1+\frac{1}{2}\right)\lambda^1 + q_2\lambda^2\right] + \left(\alpha\lambda^{1^2}+\lambda^{2^2}\right)\left[\alpha p_2\lambda^1 + \right. \\
& \left. + \left(\frac{\alpha}{2}+p^3\right)\lambda^2\right] - \varepsilon\lambda^2 - 2k_1a^2; \\
b^3 = {} & \frac{d\left(\alpha\lambda^{1^2}+\lambda^{2^2}\right)}{d\sigma} + a^1\alpha\lambda^1 + a^2\lambda^2 + \\
& + 2\left(\alpha\lambda^{1^2}+\lambda^{2^2}\right)\left(q_1\lambda^1+q_2\lambda^2-k_1\right).
\end{aligned}
\right\} \qquad (14.4)
$$

The quantities a^1, a^2 and b^1, b^2, b^3 are further related among themselves by the following:

$$
\left.
\begin{aligned}
& \frac{db^1}{d\sigma} + b^1\left[\left(q_1-\frac{1}{2}\right)\lambda^1 + q_2\lambda^2\right] + b^2\left[\frac{2\alpha p_2+q_2}{3}\lambda^1 + \right. \\
& \left. + \left(\frac{\alpha}{2}-\frac{\alpha q_1-p_1+p_3}{3}\right)\lambda^2\right] + b^3\left[\left(\frac{\alpha}{2}+p_1\right)\lambda^1 + \right. \\
& \left. + p_2\lambda^2\right] = k_2\lambda^1 + 3\varepsilon a^1 + 3k_1b^1; \\
& \frac{db^2}{d\sigma} + b^1\left[-\frac{2p_2+\alpha q_2}{3}\lambda^1 + \left(\frac{1}{2} + \right.\right. \\
& \left.\left. + \frac{q_1-\alpha p_1+\alpha p_3}{3}\right)\lambda^2\right] + b^2\left[\left(q_1+\frac{1}{2}\right)\lambda^1 + q_2\lambda^2\right] + \\
& + b^3\left[\alpha p_2\lambda^1 + \left(\frac{\alpha}{2}+p_3\right)\lambda^2\right] = k_2\lambda^2 + 3\varepsilon a^2 + 3k_1b^2; \\
& \frac{db^3}{d\sigma} + b^1\alpha\lambda^1 + b^2\lambda^2 + 2b^3\left(q_1\lambda^1+q_2\lambda^2\right) = \\
& = 3\varepsilon\left(\alpha\lambda^{1^2}+\lambda^{2^2}\right) + 3k_1b^3.
\end{aligned}
\right\} \qquad (14.5)
$$

Using equations (14.2–14.5) one can study the properties of nonplanar lines on the surface.

If the osculating plane of a line on the surface is normal to this surface at every point, then the determinant

$$|\bar{e}_3\ \bar{u}_1\ \bar{u}_2| = 0,$$

or

$$a^1\lambda^2 - a^2\lambda^1 = 0.$$

Replacing a^1, a^2 here by their expressions from (14.3) and $\lambda^1 d\sigma$, $\lambda^2 d\sigma$ by the forms ω^1, ω^2 respectively, we obtain equation (4.3).

§ 15. Exercises. Using equations (14.2–14.5), obtain the equations of lines on the surface satisfying one of the following requirements:

a) the normal planes of the line are normal to the surface;

b) the principal normals of the line coincide with the normals to the surface;

c) the binormals of the line coincide with the normals to the surface;

d) the rectifying planes of the line are normal to the surface;

e) the rectifying planes of the line are tangent to the surface.

Chapter IX

CERTAIN SURFACES

§ 1. Surfaces of the second order (quadrics). If the surface *(A)* has degenerated into a surface of the second order, then its equation has the form

$$A_{ij}x^ix^j + 2A_{0i}x^i + A_{00} = 0. \qquad (1.1)$$

This quadric is osculating to itself at any of its points. Therefore the conditions (7.2–7.3), (7.6–7.7) of Chapter V are satisfied:

$$A_{01} = 0;\ A_{02} = 0;\ A_{03} = -1;\ A_{i_1i_2} = a_{i_1i_2};\ b_{i_1} = 4A_{i_1}^{3} \qquad (1.2)$$
$$(i_1,\ i_2,\ i_3 = 1, 2).$$

From the identity of equations (7.5) and (3.2) of Chapter V

$$a_{i_1i_2i_3} = A_{i_13}a_{i_2i_3} + A_{i_23}a_{i_1i_3}.$$

Replacing A_{i_13}, A_{i_23} in the above by their expressions in (1.2 : 5) we obtain the necessary conditions for the degeneration of the surface *(A)* into a surface of the second order

$$4a_{i_1i_2i_3} = b_{i_1}a_{i_2i_3} + b_{i_2}a_{i_3i_1}, \qquad (1.3)$$

where, according to the definitions (6.9), Chapter V, and (6.2), Chapter II,

$$b_{i_1} = a^{i_2i_3}a_{i_1i_2i_3};\ a^{i_1i_3}a_{i_3i_2} = \delta^{i_1}_{i_2}. \qquad (1.4)$$

In choosing the canonical frame in Chapter V the values (8.5) and (8.7–8.8) of Chapter V were specified:

$$b_1=0;\ b_2=0;\ a_{111} = \alpha;\ a_{112} = 0;\ a_{122} = -1;\ a_{222} = 0.$$

These values are not compatible with the conditions (1.3), i.e., in choosing a frame in Chapter V surfaces of the second order were excluded. Furthermore, ruled surfaces were also excluded (§ 2, Chapter VIII).

§ 2. Affine sphere. A surface all the affine normals of which form a bundle with a center is called an affine sphere. If the radius vector of the center of this bundle $\overline{C}=\overline{A}+\lambda\overline{e}_3$, then

$$d\overline{C}\left(\omega^{\alpha} + \lambda\omega_3^{\alpha}\right)\overline{e}_{\alpha} + \left(d\lambda + \lambda\omega_3^{3}\right)\overline{e}_3 = 0$$

and

$$\omega^{\alpha} + \lambda\omega_3^{\alpha} = 0 \quad (\alpha = 1, 2); \qquad (2.1)$$

$$d\lambda + \lambda\omega_3^{3} = 0. \qquad (2.2)$$

The condition of compatibility of equations (2.1) for arbitrary λ, after replacement of the forms ω_3^{α} by their expressions in equations (9.1), Chapter V, is:

$$\alpha p_2\omega^{1^2} + (p_3 - p_1)\,\omega^1\omega^2 - p_2\omega^{2^2} = 0. \qquad (2.3)$$

This equation should be an identity in $\omega^1{:}\omega^2$ for an affine sphere.

Consequently,

$$p_1 = p_3;\ p_2 = 0; \qquad (2.4)$$

$$\lambda = -\frac{1}{\frac{\alpha}{2} + p_1}. \qquad (2.5)$$

The invariant p_1 should satisfy the requirement

$$\frac{\alpha}{2} + p_1 \neq 0. \qquad (2.6)$$

The conditions (2.4), (2.6) are necessary and sufficient for the surface *(A)* to be an affine sphere.

In conformity with formula (2.5), the radius vector of the center of the sphere is

$$\overline{C} = \overline{A} - \frac{1}{\frac{\alpha}{2} + p_1} \overline{e}_3. \qquad (2.7)$$

§ 3. Surface with parallel affine normals. For infinitesimal displacement of the point A of the surface *(A)* with parallel normals

$$d\overline{e}_3 = \lambda \overline{e}_3. \qquad (3.1)$$

Consequently,

$$\left.\begin{aligned} \omega_3^\alpha \overline{e}_\alpha &= 0; \\ \omega_3^1 = 0; \quad \omega_3^2 &= 0. \end{aligned}\right\} \qquad (3.2)$$

The conditions (3.2) of parallelism of the normals to the surface are conserved for any value of the forms ω^1 and ω^2.

Therefore, replacing the forms ω_2^1 and ω_3^2 by their expressions in equations (9.1), Chapter V and using the conditions (3.2), we obtain

$$\frac{\alpha}{2} + p_1 = 0; \quad p_2 = 0; \ \frac{\alpha}{2} + p_3 = 0. \qquad (3.3)$$

The requirements (3.3) imposed on the differential invariants of the surface are the requirements of parallelism of the normals of this surface.

§ 4. Surfaces with coplanar normals. The condition of coplanarity of all normals of the surface *(A)* with a plane containing two noncollinear fixed vectors $\overline{v}_1$ and $\overline{v}_2$ is:

$$\overline{e}_3 = \lambda^\alpha \overline{v}_\alpha \qquad (\alpha = 1, 2). \qquad (4.1)$$

Consequently,

$$\omega_3^\alpha \left(\overline{e}_\alpha + \omega_3^3 \overline{e}_3 \right) = \overline{v}_\alpha d\lambda^\alpha.$$

Replacing $\overline{e}_3$ in the above by its expression in (4.1) and the forms ω_3^i by their expressions in equations (9.1), Chapter V, we obtain

$$\left[\left(\frac{\alpha}{2} + p_1 + 2\lambda^1 q^1 \right) \overline{e}_1 + (\alpha p_2 + 2\lambda^2 q_1) \overline{e}_2 \right] \omega^1 + \\ + \left[(p_2 + 2\lambda^1 q_2) \overline{e}_1 + \left(\frac{\alpha}{2} + p_3 + 2\lambda^2 q_2 \right) \overline{e}_2 \right] \omega^2 = \overline{v}_\alpha d\lambda^\alpha. \qquad (4.2)$$

For all possible displacements of the point *A* over the surface, the vector represented by the left-hand side of equation (4.2) changes, remaining tangential to the surface *(A)* at the point *A*. The vector represented by the right-hand side of this equation remains in the plane containing the vectors $\overline{v}_1$ and $\overline{v}_2$. The tangent planes to the curved surface *(A)* are not in general parallel to the plane containing the vectors $\bar{v}_1$ and $\bar{v}_2$. Therefore the requirement (4.2) is possible only for the conditions:

$$\frac{a}{2} + p_1 + 2\lambda^1 q_1 = 0; \quad p_2 + 2\lambda^1 q_2 = 0; \tag{4.3}$$

$$ap_2 + 2\lambda^2 q_1 = 0; \quad \frac{a}{2} + p_3 + 2\lambda^2 q_2 = 0; \tag{4.4}$$

$$d\lambda^a = 0. \tag{4.5}$$

The systems (4.3) and (4.4) are compatible if

$$\left(\frac{a}{2} + p_1\right) q_2 = p_2 q_1; \quad ap_2 q_2 = \left(\frac{a}{2} + p_3\right) q_1. \tag{4.6}$$

The relation (4.6) between the differential invariants expresses the requirement of coplanarity of all normals of the surface *(A)*.

The requirement (4.6) is satisfied by the values

$$q_1 = 0; \quad q_2 = 0. \tag{4.7}$$

If these values do not hold, then, from (4.6),

$$1 + 2a(p_1 + p_3) + 4p_1 p_3 - 4ap_2^2 = 0. \tag{4.8}$$

For the condition (4.7) the infinitesimal displacements of the unit point E_3 on the normal are parallel to the tangent plane to the surface at the radix of this normal.

§ 5. The surfaces (*D*), (*S*) and (*D, S*). Given the points of one Darboux line of the family ω^2 on the surface *(A)* (§ 13, Chapter VIII), let tangents be drawn at these points to the conjugate (Segrè) lines. The ruled surface (D_1) generated by these tangents is developable (§ 3, Chapter VII). The surface *(A)* will be called a *(D)* surface if to the lines ω^2 of the Darboux family correspond cylindrical surfaces (D_1). It follows from formula (3.2) of Chapter VII that to the *(D)* surfaces corresponds the following condition imposed on the differential invariants:

$$\frac{1}{2} + \frac{q_1 - ap_1 + ap_3}{3} = 0. \tag{5.1}$$

Now let tangents be drawn at the points of one Segrè line of the family ω^1 on the surface *(A)* to the conjugate (Darboux) lines. The ruled surface (S_1) generated by these tangents is developable (§ 3, Chapter VII).

The surface *(A)* will be called an *(S)* surface if to the lines ω^1 of the Segrè family correspond cylindrical surfaces ( ). It follows from formula (3.3) of Chapter VII that to *(S)* surfaces corresponds the following condition imposed on the differential invariants:

$$2ap_2 + q_2 = 0. \tag{5.2}$$

If the surface *(A)* is simultaneously a *(D)* and an *(S)* surface, we will call it a *(D, S)* surface. To such surfaces correspond the two conditions (5.1) and (5.2).

§ 6. Surfaces and certain conditions of motion of unit points of the canonical frame. The unit points E_1, E_2, E_3 of the chosen canonical frame $(A, \bar{e}_1, \bar{e}_2, \bar{e}_3)$ (Chapter V) are defined by the affine properties of the surface in the neighborhood of the point *A* (§ 9, Chapter VI).

Therefore to definite limitations of the motions of these points for definite motions of the point *A* over the surface correspond certain relations between the differential invariants of the surface (other than the equations of structure). Let us consider some of these conditions.

If the point A describes a Segrè line ($\omega^2=0$), then the unit points E_1, E_2, E_3 of the canonical frame $(A, \bar{e}_1, \bar{e}_2, \bar{e}_3)$ describe the lines (E_1), (E_2), (E_3); the tangents to these lines at points corresponding to the initial position of the point A are parallel respectively to the vectors given by formulas (1.4–1.6) of Chapter VII. To those surfaces for which, for displacement of the point A along the Segrè line $d\bar{A}=\omega^1\bar{e}_1$, the tangent to the line (E_1) at the point E_1 corresponding to the point A–1) lies on the plane x^1Ax^3, 2) is parallel to the plane x^2Ax^3, or 3) is parallel to the normal Ax^3, correspond the conditions imposed on the differential invariants

$$2p_2 + aq_2 = 0 \tag{6.1}$$

or

$$q_1 + \frac{1}{2} = 0, \tag{6.2}$$

or

$$2p_2 + aq_2 = 0; \quad q_1 + \frac{1}{2} = 0. \tag{6.3}$$

It follows from (1.5), Chapter VII, that for condition (6.2) the tangent to the line (E_2) at the corresponding point E_2 is parallel to the Ax^1 axis. The condition

$$1 + \frac{2ap_2 + q_2}{3} = 0 \tag{6.4}$$

means that for displacement of the point A along the Segrè line ($d\bar{A}=\omega^1\bar{e}_1$) the line (E_2) osculates with the Ax^2 axis at the point E_2, i.e., the Ax^2 axes of the canonical frames of the surface at points of the Segrè line $\omega^2 = 0$ passing through the point A are generators of the developable surface with the edge of regression (E_2).

For example, with the aid of formulas (1.4–1.6) of Chapter VII and (2.4–2.6) of Chapter VII one can distinguish various surfaces with definite affine properties.

Chapter X

RULED SURFACES

§ 1. Choice of a canonical frame. The frame obtained in Chapter V refers to unruled surfaces (§ 2, Chapter VIII). If the surface (A) is skew ruled, then all its points are of the hyperbolic type. Placing the Ax^1, Ax^2 axes of the frame $(A, \bar{e}_1, \bar{e}_2, \bar{e}_3)$ in the tangent plane to such a surface at the point A, we obtain in equations (7.1) of the Introduction:

$$\omega^3 = 0. \tag{1.1}$$

After three-fold continuation of this equation, we obtain the system (3.1–3.3) of Chapter V

$$\left.\begin{aligned} \omega_{i_1}^3 &= a_{i_1 i_2}\omega^{i_2} \quad (i_1, i_2, i_3 = 1,2); \\ da_{i_1 i_2} &= a_{i_3 i_1}\omega_{i_2}^{i_3} + a_{i_3 i_2}\omega_{i_1}^{i_3} - a_{i_1 i_2}\omega_3^3 + a_{i_1 i_2 i_3}\omega^{i_3}; \end{aligned}\right\} \tag{1.2}$$

$$da_{i_1 i_2 i_3} = a_{i_4 i_1 i_2}\omega_{i_3}^{i_4} + a_{i_4 i_2 i_3}\omega_{i_1}^{i_4} + a_{i_4 i_3 i_2}\omega_{i_2}^{i_4} - a_{i_1 i_2 i_3}\omega_3^3 +$$
$$+ (a_{i_4 i_1} a_{i_2 i_3} + a_{i_4 i_2} a_{i_3 i_1} + a_{i_4 i_3} a_{i_1 i_2})\omega_3^{i_4} + a_{i_1 i_2 i_3 i_4}\omega^{i_4}. \tag{1.2}$$

Set

$$a_{11} = 1;\ a_{12} = 0;\ a_{22} = -1. \tag{1.3}$$

Therefore, from equation (1.2 : 1) we obtain

$$\omega_1^3 = \omega^1;\ \ \omega_2^3 = -\omega^2. \tag{1.4}$$

It follows from equation (4.10), Chapter V, that, for the values of $a_{i_1 i_2}$ in (1.3), the Ax^1 and Ax^2 axes are conjugate with respect to the surface (A) and the point A. The coordinates of the vector $d\bar{A} = \omega^a \bar{e}_a$ $(a=1,2)$ with asymptotic direction satisfy the equation

$$\omega^{1^2} - \omega^{2^2} = 0. \tag{1.5}$$

To each of the two asymptotic directions issuing from the point A corresponds one of the following conditions:

$$\omega^2 = \omega^1 \tag{1.6}$$

or

$$\omega^2 = -\omega^1. \tag{1.7}$$

If a straight line lies on the surface (A), then for displacement of the point A along it the coordinates ω^a of the displacement vector $d\bar{A}$ should satisfy the equation (§ 2, Chapter VIII) $d^2\bar{A} = \lambda d\bar{A}$, or

$$\omega^2 d\omega^1 - \omega^1 d\omega^2 + \omega^2\omega^a\omega_a^1 - \omega^1\omega^a\omega_a^2 = 0. \tag{1.8}$$

Since a straight line on the surface is an asymptotic line on it (§ 2, Chapter VIII), assuming that the coordinates ω^a of the vector $d\bar{A}$ satisfy equation (1.6), we obtain from (1.8) the following condition on secondary forms:

$$\omega_1^1 - \omega_2^2 + \omega_2^1 - \omega_1^2 = 0. \tag{1.9}$$

Replacing the quantities $a_{i_1 i_2}$ in equation (1.2 : 2) by their values in (1.3), we obtain

$$\left.\begin{aligned} 2\omega_1^1 - \omega_3^3 &= -a_{11a}\omega^a; \\ \omega_2^1 - \omega_1^2 &= -a_{12a}\omega^a; \\ \omega_3^3 - 2\omega_2^2 &= -a_{22a}\omega^a. \end{aligned}\right\} \tag{1.10}$$

It follows from the above equations that the condition (1.9) imposes two restrictions on the quantities $a_{i_1 i_2 i_3}$:

$$\left.\begin{aligned} a_{111} + 2a_{112} + a_{122} &= 0; \\ a_{222} + a_{112} + 2a_{122} &= 0. \end{aligned}\right\} \tag{1.11}$$

For constant $a_{i_1 i_2 i_3}$, we obtain from equation (1.2 : 3) the system

$$\left.\begin{aligned} &\frac{1}{2}a_{111}\omega_3^3 + 3a_{112}\omega_1^2 + 3\omega_3^1 + \left(a_{111a} - \frac{3}{2}a_{111}a_{11a}\right)\omega^a = 0; \\ &\frac{1}{2}a_{112}\omega_3^3 + (a_{111} + 2a_{122})\,\omega_1^2 - \omega_2^2 + \Big[a_{112}\left(\frac{1}{2}a_{22a} - \right. \\ &\qquad \left. - a_{11a}\right) - a_{111}a_{12a} + a_{112a}\Big]\,\omega^a = 0; \end{aligned}\right| \tag{1.12}$$

$$\left.\begin{aligned}&\frac{1}{2}a_{122}\omega_2^3+(a_{222}+2a_{112})\,\omega_1^2-\omega_3^1+\Big[a_{122}\Big(a_{22\alpha}-\\&\quad-\frac{1}{2}a_{11\alpha}\Big)-2a_{112}a_{12\alpha}+a_{122\alpha}\Big]\,\omega^\alpha=0;\\&\frac{1}{2}a_{222}\,\omega_3^3+3a_{122}\omega_1^2+3\omega_3^2+\Big(\frac{3}{2}a_{222}a_{22\alpha}-\\&\quad-3a_{122}a_{12\alpha}+a_{222\alpha}\Big)\,\omega^\alpha=0.\end{aligned}\right\}\qquad(1.12)$$

If we could solve the system of four equations (1.12) for ω_3^3, ω_1^2, ω_3^1, ω_3^2 for certain values of $a_{i_1i_2i_3}$, we would obtain a definite canonical frame of the surface under consideration.

Under (1.11) the determinant of this system

$$\frac{1}{2}\begin{vmatrix}a_{111} & 3a_{112} & 3 & 0\\ a_{112} & a_{111}+2a_{122} & 0 & -1\\ a_{122} & a_{222}+2a_{112} & -1 & 0\\ a_{222} & 3a_{122} & 0 & 3\end{vmatrix}$$

is zero. To the values of $a_{i_1i_2}$ in (1.3) correspond the values

$$a^{11}=1;\ a^{12}=0;\ a^{22}=-1;\qquad(1.13)$$

of the quantities $a^{i_1i_2}$ which are defined by

$$a_{i_1i_3}a^{i_3i_2}=\delta_{i_1}^{i_2}.\qquad(1.14)$$

Therefore

$$\left.\begin{aligned}b_1&=a^{i_1i_2}a_{i_1i_21}=a_{111}-a_{122};\\ b_2&=a^{i_1i_2}a_{i_1i_22}=a_{112}-a_{222}.\end{aligned}\right\}\qquad(1.15)$$

Let us add to the conditions (1.11) the requirement

$$b_1=b_2=0,\qquad(1.16)$$

or

$$a_{111}=a_{122};\ a_{112}=a_{222}.\qquad(1.17)$$

Set

$$a_{111}=a_{122}=-1.\qquad(1.18)$$

Therefore, in conformity with the conditions (1.11) and (1.17), we obtain

$$a_{222}=a_{112}=1.\qquad(1.19)$$

Replacing $a_{i_1i_2i_3}$ by their values in (1.18–1.19), we can write equations (1.10) and (1.12) in the form

$$\left.\begin{aligned}2\omega_1^1-\omega_3^3&=\omega^1-\omega^2;\\ \omega_2^1-\omega_1^2&=-\omega^1+\omega^2;\\ \omega_3^3-2\omega_2^2&=\omega^1-\omega^2.\end{aligned}\right\}\qquad(1.20)$$

$$\left.\begin{aligned}\frac{1}{2}\omega_3^3-3\omega_1^2-3\omega_3^1&=\Big(a_{111}-\frac{3}{2}\Big)\omega^1+\Big(a_{1112}+\frac{3}{2}\Big)\omega^2;\\ -\frac{1}{2}\omega_3^3+3\omega_1^2+\omega_3^2&=\Big(a_{1112}+\frac{3}{2}\Big)\omega^1+\Big(a_{1122}-\frac{3}{2}\Big)\omega^2;\\ \frac{1}{2}\omega_3^3-3\omega_1^2+\omega_3^1&=\Big(a_{1122}-\frac{3}{2}\Big)\omega^1+\Big(a_{1222}+\frac{3}{2}\Big)\omega^2;\\ -\frac{1}{2}\omega_3^3+3\omega_1^2-3\omega_3^2&=\Big(a_{1222}+\frac{3}{2}\Big)\omega^1+\Big(a_{2222}-\frac{3}{2}\Big)\omega^2.\end{aligned}\right\}\qquad(1.21)$$

To the linear dependence of the left-hand sides of equations (1.12) corresponds a similar dependence of their right-hand sides. But since the principal forms ω^1 and ω^2 are linearly independent,

$$\begin{aligned} a_{1111}+3a_{1112}+3a_{1122}+a_{1222}&=0;\\ a_{1112}+3a_{1122}+3a_{1222}+a_{2222}&=0. \end{aligned} \tag{1.22}$$

Another continuation is necessary to choose the canonical frame.

By exterior differentiations of equation (1.2 : 3), we obtain

$$\begin{aligned} da_{i_1\cdots i_4}={}&a_{i_5i_1i_2i_3}\omega_{i_4}^{i_5}+a_{i_5i_2i_3i_4}\omega_{i_1}^{i_5}+a_{i_5i_3i_4i_1}\omega_{i_2}^{i_5}+a_{i_5i_4i_1i_2}\omega_{i_3}^{i_5}-\\ &-a_{i_1\cdots i_4}\omega_3^3+\left(a_{i_5i_1}a_{i_2i_3i_4}+a_{i_5i_2}a_{i_3i_4i_1}+a_{i_5i_3}a_{i_4i_1i_2}+a_{i_5i_4}a_{i_1i_2i_2}\right)\omega_3^{i_5}+\\ &+\left(a_{i_5i_1i_2}a_{i_3i_4}+a_{i_5i_2i_3}a_{i_4i_1}+a_{i_5i_3i_4}a_{i_1i_2}+a_{i_5i_4i_1}a_{i_2i_3}+a_{i_5i_2i_4}a_{i_1i_2}+\right.\\ &\left.+a_{i_5i_1i_3}a_{i_2i_4}\right)\omega_3^{i_5}+a_{i_1\cdots i_4i_5}\omega^{i_5}. \end{aligned} \tag{1.23}$$

Set

$$a_{1122}=0. \tag{1.24}$$

For this value equations (1.22), (1.21) and (1.23) can be written in the form

$$\left.\begin{aligned} a_{1111}&=-3a_{1112}-a_{1222};\\ a_{2222}&=-a_{1112}-3a_{1222}. \end{aligned}\right\} \tag{1.25}$$

$$\left.\begin{aligned} &\frac{1}{2}\omega_3^3-3\omega_1^2-3\omega_3^1=-\left(3a_{1112}+a_{1222}+\frac{3}{2}\right)\omega^1+\\ &\qquad+\left(a_{1112}+\frac{3}{2}\right)\omega^2;\\ &-\frac{1}{2}\omega_3^3+3\omega_1^2+\omega_3^2=\left(a_{1112}+\frac{3}{2}\right)\omega^1-\frac{3}{2}\omega^2;\\ &\frac{1}{2}\omega_3^3-3\omega_1^2+\omega_3^1=\frac{-3}{2}\omega^1+\left(a_{1222}+\frac{3}{2}\right)\omega^2; \end{aligned}\right\} \tag{1.26}$$

$$a_{1112}\omega_2^1+a_{1222}\omega_1^2-\omega_3^1-\omega_3^2+\frac{1}{2}a_{1122\alpha}\omega^\alpha=0. \tag{1.27}$$

In the system of equations (1.26) the last equation of (1.21) is absent, being a corollary of the first three equations.

Solving the seven equations (1.26) and (1.20) for the seven unknowns

$$\omega_3^1,\ \omega_3^2,\ \omega_1^2,\ \omega_2^1,\ \omega_3^3,\ \omega_1^1,\ \omega_2^2,$$

we obtain

$$\left.\begin{aligned} \omega_3^1&=\left(\frac{3}{4}a_{1112}+\frac{1}{4}a_{1222}\right)\omega^1+\left(\frac{1}{4}a_{1222}-\frac{1}{4}a_{1112}\right)\omega^2;\\ \omega_3^2&=\left(\frac{1}{4}a_{1112}-\frac{1}{4}a_{1222}\right)\omega^1+\left(\frac{3}{4}a_{1222}+\frac{1}{4}a_{1112}\right)\omega^2;\\ \omega_1^2&=\frac{2a_{1112}-\frac{1}{2}a_{11122}}{a_{1112}+a_{1222}}\omega^1+\frac{a_{1222}-a_{1112}-\frac{1}{2}a_{11222}}{a_{1112}+a_{1222}}\omega^2;\\ \omega_2^1&=\frac{a_{1112}-a_{1222}-\frac{1}{2}a_{11122}}{a_{1112}+a_{1222}}\omega^1+\frac{2a_{1222}-\frac{1}{2}a_{11222}}{a_{1112}+a_{1222}}\omega^2; \end{aligned}\right\} \tag{1.28}$$

$$\left.\begin{aligned}
\omega_3^3 &= \left(6\,\frac{2a_{1112}-\frac{1}{2}a_{11122}}{a_{1112}+a_{1222}}-\frac{3}{2}a_{1112}-\frac{1}{2}a_{1222}-3\right)\omega^1+\\
&+\left(6\,\frac{a_{1222}-a_{1112}-\frac{1}{2}a_{11222}}{a_{1112}+a_{1222}}+\frac{3}{2}a_{1222}+\frac{1}{2}a_{1112}+3\right)\omega^2;\\
\omega_1^1 &= \left(3\,\frac{2a_{1112}-\frac{1}{2}a_{11122}}{a_{1112}+a_{1222}}-\frac{3}{4}a_{1112}-\frac{1}{4}a_{1222}-1\right)\omega^1+\\
&+\left(3\,\frac{a_{1222}-a_{1112}-\frac{1}{2}a_{11222}}{a_{1112}+a_{1222}}+\frac{3}{4}a_{1222}+\frac{1}{4}a_{1112}+1\right)\omega^2;\\
\omega_2^2 &= \left(3\,\frac{2a_{1112}-\frac{1}{2}a_{11122}}{a_{1112}+a_{1222}}-\frac{3}{4}a_{1112}-\frac{1}{4}a_{1222}-2\right)\omega^1+\\
&+\left(3\,\frac{a_{1222}-a_{1112}-\frac{1}{2}a_{11222}}{a_{1112}+a_{1222}}+\frac{3}{4}a_{1222}+\frac{1}{4}a_{1112}+2\right)\omega^2.
\end{aligned}\right\}\qquad(1.28)$$

The frame is chosen. Let us set

$$\left.\begin{aligned}
4p_1 &= 3a_{1112}+a_{1222};\\
4p_2 &= 3a_{1222}+a_{1112};\\
2q_1 &= \frac{3a_{1112}-a_{1222}-a_{11122}}{a_{1112}+a_{1222}};\\
2q_2 &= \frac{3a_{1222}-a_{1112}-a_{11222}}{a_{1112}+a_{1222}}.
\end{aligned}\right\}\qquad(1.29)$$

In the above notation of the four differential invariants p_1, p_2, q_1, q_2 equations (1.28) can be written as

$$\left.\begin{aligned}
&\omega_3^1 = p_1\omega^1+\frac{p_2-p_1}{2}\omega^2;\qquad \omega_3^2=\frac{p_1-p_2}{2}\omega^1+p_2\omega^2;\\
&\omega_1^2=\left(q_1+\frac{1}{2}\right)\omega^1+\left(q_2-\frac{1}{2}\right)\omega^2,\\
&\omega_2^1=\left(q_1-\frac{1}{2}\right)\omega^1+\left(q_2+\frac{1}{2}\right)\omega^2;\\
&\omega_3^3=(6q_1-2p_1)\,\omega^1+(6q_2+2p_2)\,\omega^2;\\
&\omega_1^1=\left(3q_1-p_1+\frac{1}{2}\right)\omega^1+\left(3q_2+p_2-\frac{1}{2}\right)\omega^2;\\
&\omega_2^2=\left(3q_1-p_1-\frac{1}{2}\right)\omega^1+\left(3q_2+p_2+\frac{1}{2}\right)\omega^2.
\end{aligned}\right\}\qquad(1.30)$$

In formulas (1.4) and (1.30) all the secondary forms ω_i^j refer to a ring with a basis of principal forms ω^1 and ω^2.

§ 2. Darboux-Cartan formulas. Let us replace in equations (1.2) of Chapter V the form ω^3 by its value in (1.1) and all secondary forms by their expressions in (1.4) and (1.30). We obtain the equations for infinitesimal displacements of the chosen canonical frame.

Let us write them down by convention in the form

	$\bar{e}_1$	$\bar{e}_2$	$\bar{e}_3$
$d\bar{A}$	ω^1	ω^2	0
$d\bar{e}_1$	$\left(3q_1-p_1+\frac{1}{2}\right)\omega^1+$ $+\left(3q_2+p_2-\frac{1}{2}\right)\omega^2$	$\left(q_1+\frac{1}{2}\right)\omega^1+$ $+\left(q_2-\frac{1}{2}\right)\omega^2$	ω^1
$d\bar{e}_2$	$\left(q_1-\frac{1}{2}\right)\omega^1+$ $+\left(q_2+\frac{1}{2}\right)\omega^2$	$\left(3q_1-p_1-\frac{1}{2}\right)\omega^1+$ $+\left(3q_2+p_2+\frac{1}{2}\right)\omega^2$	$-\omega^2$
$d\bar{e}_3$	$p_1\omega^1+\frac{p_2-p_1}{2}\omega^2$	$\frac{p_1-p_2}{2}\omega^1+p_2\omega^2$	$(6q_1-2p_1)\omega^1+$ $+(6q_2+2p_2)\omega^2$

(2.1)

The equations of structure corresponding to the system of equations (2.1) are:

$$\left.\begin{aligned}
&D\omega^1=(p_2-q_1+3q_2)\,[\omega^1\omega^2],\quad D\omega^2=(p_1-3q_1+q_2)\,[\omega^1\omega^2];\\
&[d\,(3q_1-p_1),\,\omega^1]+[d\,(3q_2+p_2),\,\omega^2]+(3q_2^2-3q_1^2+\\
&\qquad+p_1q_1+p_2q_2)\,[\omega^1\omega^2]=0;\\
&[dq_1\omega^1]+[dq_2\omega^2]+\Big(q_2^2-q_1^2+p_1q_2+p_2q_1-\\
&\qquad-\frac{1}{2}p_1-\frac{1}{2}p_2\Big)[\omega^1\omega^2]=0;\\
&[dp_1\omega^1]+\frac{1}{2}[d\,(p_2-p_1),\,\omega^2]+\{(p_2-p_1)(p_1-2q_1+q_2)+\\
&\qquad+2p_1(p_2+3q_2)\}\,[\omega^1\omega^2]=0;\\
&\frac{1}{2}[d\,(p_1-p_2),\,\omega^1]+[dp_2\omega^2]+\{(p_1-p_2)(p_2-q_1+2q_2)+\\
&\qquad+2p_2(p_1-3q_1)\}\,[\omega^1\omega^2]=0.
\end{aligned}\right\}\quad(2.2)$$

§ 3. Canonical expansion of the coordinates of the generic point of the surface. The first equation of the system (2.1) and two others obtained from it by successive differentiation can be written with the aid of this system as follows:

$$\left.\begin{aligned}
&d\bar{A}=\omega^1\bar{e}_1+\omega^2\bar{e}_2;\\
&d^2\bar{A}=\Big[d\omega^1+\Big(3q_1-p_1+\frac{1}{2}\Big)\omega^{1^2}+(q_1+3q_2+p_2-1)\,\omega^1\omega^2+\\
&+\Big(q_2+\frac{1}{2}\Big)\omega^{2^2}\Big]\bar{e}_1+\Big[d\omega^2+\Big(q_1+\frac{1}{2}\Big)\omega^{1^2}+(3q_1+q_2-\\
&-p_1-1)\,\omega^1\omega^2+\Big(3q_2+p_2+\frac{1}{2}\Big)\omega^{2^2}\Big]\bar{e}_2+(\omega^{1^2}-\omega^{2^2})\,\bar{e}_3;\\
&d^3\bar{A}=a^1\bar{e}_1+a^2\bar{e}_2+\Big[3\,(\omega^1d\omega^1-\omega^2d\omega^2)+\Big(9q_1-3p_1+\\
&\qquad+\frac{1}{2}\Big)\omega^{1^3}+\Big(9q_2+3p_2-\frac{3}{2}\Big)\omega^{1^2}\omega^2+\Big(3p_1-9q_1+\\
&\qquad+\frac{3}{2}\Big)\omega^1\omega^{2^2}-\Big(9q_2+3p_2+\frac{1}{2}\Big)\omega^{2^3}\Big]\bar{e}_3.
\end{aligned}\right\}\quad(3.1)$$

Replacing the first three differentials in the expansion (10.1), Chapter V of the vector function $\bar{A}\,(\omega^1,\,\omega^2)$ by their expressions in (3.1), we obtain

$$\overline{A}(\omega^1, \omega^2) = \Big\{\omega^1 + \frac{1}{2}\Big[d\omega^1 + \Big(3q_1 - p_1 + \frac{1}{2}\Big)\omega^{1^2} + $$
$$+ (q_1 + 3q_2 + p_2 - 1)\,\omega^1\omega^2 + \Big(q_2 + \frac{1}{2}\Big)\omega^{2^2}\Big] + \dots\Big\}\overline{e}_1 +$$
$$+ \Big\{\omega^2 + \frac{1}{2}\Big[d\omega^2 + \Big(q_1 + \frac{1}{2}\Big)\omega^{1^2} + (3q_1 + q_2 - p_1 - 1)\,\omega^1\omega^2 +$$
$$+ \Big(3q_2 + p + \frac{1}{2}\Big)\omega^{2^2} + \dots\Big\}\overline{e}_2 + \Big\{\frac{1}{2}(\omega^{1^2} - \omega^{2^2}) +$$
$$+ \frac{1}{6}\Big[3(\omega^1 d\omega^1 - \omega^2 d\omega^2) + \Big(9q_1 - 3p_1 + \frac{1}{2}\Big)\omega^{1^3} +$$
$$+ \Big(9q_2 + 3p_2 - \frac{3}{2}\Big)\omega^{1^2}\omega^2 + \Big(3p_1 - 9q_1 + \frac{3}{2}\Big)\omega^1\omega^{2^2} -$$
$$- \Big(9q_2 + 3p_2 + \frac{1}{2}\Big)\omega^{2^3}\Big] + \dots\Big\}\overline{e}_3. \qquad (3.2)$$

If x^1, x^2, x^3 are the current coordinates of the point $A\ (\omega^1, \omega^2)$ on the surface (A) with reference to the chosen canonical frame $(A, \overline{e}_1, \overline{e}_2, \overline{e}_3)$, then from equation (3.2) we obtain the canonical expansion of the coordinates of the generic point of the surface:

$$\left.\begin{aligned}
x^1 &= \omega^1 + \frac{1}{2}\Big[d\omega^1 + \Big(3q_1 - p_1 + \frac{1}{2}\Big)\omega^{1^2} + (q_1 + 3q_2 + \\
&\quad + p_2 - 1)\,\omega^1\omega^2 + \Big(q_2 + \frac{1}{2}\Big)\omega^{2^2}\Big] + \dots \\
x^2 &= \omega^2 + \frac{1}{2}\Big[d\omega^2 + \Big(q_1 + \frac{1}{2}\Big)\omega^{1^2} + (3q_1 + q_2 - p_1 - 1)\omega^1\omega^2 + \\
&\quad + \Big(3q_2 + p_2 + \frac{1}{2}\Big)\omega^{2^2}\Big] + \dots \\
x^3 &= \frac{1}{2}(\omega^{1^2} - \omega^{2^2}) + \frac{1}{6}\Big[3(\omega^1 d\omega^1 - \omega^2 d\omega^2) + \Big(9q_1 - 3p_1 + \\
&\quad + \frac{1}{2}\Big)\omega^{1^3} + \Big(9q_2 + 3p_2 - \frac{3}{2}\Big)\omega^{1^2}\omega^2 + \Big(3p_1 - 9q_1 + \\
&\quad + \frac{3}{2}\Big)\omega^1\omega^{2^2} - \Big(9q_2 + 3p_2 + \frac{1}{2}\Big)\omega^{2^3}\Big] + \dots
\end{aligned}\right\} \qquad (3.3)$$

Restricting ourselves to the leading terms of the expansions (3.3), we obtain the equations of an osculating hyperbolic paraboloid:

$$x^1 = \omega^1;\ x^2 = \omega^2;\ x^3 = \frac{1}{2}(\omega^{1^2} - \omega^{2^2}), \qquad (3.4)$$

or, in implicit form,

$$2x^3 = x^{1^2} - x^{2^2}. \qquad (3.5)$$

Let us express the equation of the surface in the form (10.5) of Chapter V. Replacing the coordinates x^1, x^2, x^3 in this equation by their expressions in (3.3) and comparing the infinitesimals up to the fourth order in the resulting identity, we obtain

$$a_1 = \frac{1}{2};\ a_2 = 0;\ a_3 = -\frac{1}{2};\ b_1 = -\frac{1}{6};\ b_2 = \frac{1}{2};$$
$$b_3 = -\frac{1}{2};\ b_4 = \frac{1}{6}.$$

Calculating the terms of the expansion (10.5), Chapter V, up to the fourth degree, we obtain the equation of the surface (A) in the form

$$2x^3 = x^{1^2} - x^{2^2} - \frac{1}{3}(x^1 - x^2)^3 + 0(4). \tag{3.6}$$

§ 4. Pencil of Darboux quadrics. Affine normal. Equation (7.8) of Chapter V for a pencil of Darboux quadrics becomes, with the conditions (1.3) and (1.16),

$$x^{1^2} - x^{2^2} - 2x^3 + A_{33}x^{3^2} = 0. \tag{4.1}$$

With the condition

$$A_{33} = 0$$

we recover equation (3.5). The affine normal to the surface (A) at the point A – the Ax^3 axis of the chosen canonical frame – contains the centers of the osculating Darboux quadrics (4.1).

§ 5. The family of planes conjugate to the tangents to the normal section of the surface. The condition for conjugation (4.10), Chapter V, of the vectors

$$d_\beta \overline{A} = \underset{\beta}{\omega^\alpha} \overline{e}_\alpha \quad (\alpha, \beta = 1, 2)$$

with respect to the surface under consideration and the point A is

$$\underset{1}{\omega^1}\underset{2}{\omega^1} - \underset{1}{\omega^2}\underset{2}{\omega^2} = 0.$$

Therefore the vector conjugate to the vector

$$d\overline{A} = \omega^1 \overline{e}_1 + \omega^2 \overline{e}_2 \tag{5.1}$$

is

$$d_\sigma \overline{A} = \omega^2 \overline{e}_1 + \omega^1 \overline{e}_2. \tag{5.2}$$

Let

$$\sigma^\alpha = \sigma^\alpha(\sigma) \quad (\alpha = 1, 2) \tag{5.3}$$

be the equations of the line on the surface; the forms ω^α, ω^{ji} become respectively $\lambda^\alpha d\sigma$, $\lambda_i^j d\sigma$ ((5.2–5.3), Chapter VI). The equations of the normal plane conjugate to the vector $d\overline{A}$, if X is the radius vector of the generic point of this plane, can be written in the form

$$\left| \overline{X} - \overline{A}, \overline{e}_3, \frac{d_c\overline{A}}{d\sigma} \right| = 0. \tag{5.4}$$

If the point A moves along the normal section, then equations (5.6–5.7) of Chapter VI become

$$\left.\begin{aligned} &\frac{d\overline{A}}{d\sigma} = \lambda^1 \overline{e}_1 + \lambda^2 \overline{e}_2; \\ &\frac{d\overline{A}}{d\sigma^2} = \left(\frac{d\lambda^1}{d\sigma} + \lambda^1\lambda_1^1 + \lambda^2\lambda_2^1\right)\overline{e}_1 + \left(\frac{d\lambda^2}{d\sigma} + \lambda^1\lambda_1^2 + \lambda^2\lambda_2^2\right)\overline{e}_2 + \\ &\quad + \left(\lambda^{1^2} - \lambda^{2^2}\right)\overline{e}_2 \end{aligned}\right\} \tag{5.5}$$

and

$$\frac{d\lambda^1}{d\sigma} + \lambda^1\lambda_1^1 + \lambda^2\lambda_2^1 = \varphi\lambda^1; \quad \frac{d\lambda^2}{d\sigma} + \lambda^1\lambda_1^2 + \lambda^2\lambda_2^2 = \varphi\lambda^2. \tag{5.6}$$

Formula (5.5 : 2) was obtained with the aid of equations (2.1). Let us obtain, on the plane (5.4) corresponding to the point A, the characteristic of the family of such planes at points of the line (5.3) under the condition (5.6). Differentiating equation (5.4) with respect to σ, we obtain

$$\left|\overline{X}-\overline{A},\ \lambda_3^i\overline{e}_i,\ \lambda^2\overline{e}_1+\lambda^1\overline{e}_2\right|+\left|\overline{X}-\overline{A},\overline{e}_3,\ \left(\frac{d\lambda^2}{d\sigma}+\lambda^2\lambda_1^1+\lambda^1\lambda_2^1\right)\overline{e}_1+\right.$$
$$\left.+\left(\frac{d\lambda^1}{d\sigma}+\lambda^2\lambda_1^2+\lambda^1\lambda_2^2\right)\overline{e}_2\right|=\left|\lambda^1\overline{e}_1+\lambda^2\overline{e}_2,\ \overline{e}_3,\ \lambda^2\overline{e}_1+\lambda^1\overline{e}_2\right|. \qquad (5.7)$$

We express the radius vector $\overline{X}-\overline{A}$ with reference to the frame $(A, \overline{e}_1, \overline{e}_2, \overline{e}_3)$ in the form

$$\overline{X}-\overline{A}=x^i\overline{e}_i. \qquad (5.8)$$

The equation of the plane (5.7) corresponding to the point A with reference to the frame $(A, \overline{e}_1, \overline{e}_2, \overline{e}_3)$ can be written as

$$\left[\left(\varphi-\lambda_1^1+\lambda_2^2+\lambda_3^3\right)\lambda^1+\left(\lambda_1^2-\lambda_2^1\right)\lambda^2\right]x^1+\left[\left(\lambda_1^2-\lambda_2^1\right)\lambda^1+\right.$$
$$\left.+\left(\lambda_2^2-\lambda_3^3-\lambda_1^1-\varphi\right)\lambda^2\right]x^2+\left(\lambda^2\lambda_3^2-\lambda_3^1\lambda^1\right)x^3={\lambda^1}^2-{\lambda^2}^2. \qquad (5.9)$$

The derivatives $\frac{d\lambda^1}{d\sigma}$ and $\frac{d\lambda^2}{d\sigma}$ have been replaced by their expressions in (5.6). The equation of the plane (5.4) with reference to the frame (A, e_1, e_2, e_3) is

$$\lambda^1x^1-\lambda^2x^2=0. \qquad (5.10)$$

The required characteristic is the straight line of intersection of the planes (5.9) and (5.10). The point of intersection of this characteristic and the tangent plane to the surface (A) at the point A is obtained by adjoining to equations (5.9–5.10) the equation of this tangent plane with reference to the same canonical frame:

$$x^3=0. \qquad (5.11)$$

Solving the system (5.9–5.11) for x^1, x^2, x^3 and using equations (2.1), we obtain the coordinates of the required point in the form

$$x^1=\frac{{\lambda^1}^2-{\lambda^2}^2}{(\lambda^1-\lambda^2)^3}\lambda^2;\quad x^2=\frac{{\lambda^1}^2-{\lambda^2}^2}{(\lambda^1-\lambda^2)^3}\lambda^1;\quad x^3=0. \qquad (5.12)$$

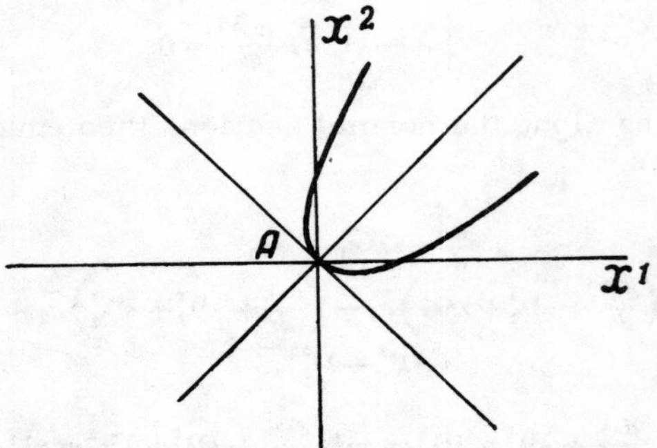

FIGURE 5

These equations are the equations of the indicatrix of the characteristics of the normal planes (§ 6, Chapter VI). Eliminating the parameter $\lambda^1:\lambda^2$ from equations (5.12 : 1–2), we obtain the equation of this line in implicit form. This equation is of the third order (Figure 5) and breaks up into a straight line and a parabola, the equations of which are respectively

$$x^1 = x^2 \tag{5.13}$$

and

$$(x^2 - x^1)^2 = x^1 + x^2. \tag{5.14}$$

§ 6. Indicatrix of characteristics of normal planes. The equations of the line of intersection of an osculating paraboloid (3.5) and the plane parallel to the tangent plane to the surface (A) at the point A are, in the canonical frame $(A, \bar{e}_1, \bar{e}_2, \bar{e}_3)$,

$$2x^3 = x^{1^2} - x^{2^2}; \quad x^3 = h. \tag{6.1}$$

The equation of the projection of this line onto the tangent plane x^1Ax^2 parallel to the affine normal Ax^3 is, in the frame $(A, \bar{e}_1, \bar{e}_2)$,

$$x^{1^2} - x^{2^2} = 2h. \tag{6.2}$$

To the family of the indicated parallel planes corresponds the one-parameter family of hyperbolas $(h \neq 0)$ (6.2) with common asymptotes

$$x^1 = x^2 \tag{6.3}$$

and

$$x^1 + x^2 = 0. \tag{6.4}$$

The above are straight lines with asymptotic directions relative to the surface (A) and the point A. The equation of the tangent to the line (6.2) at the point $M(x^1, x^2)$ is:

$$x^1y^1 - x^2y^2 = 2h, \tag{6.5}$$

where y^1, y^2 are the current coordinates.

The directions of the straight line AM and the tangent (6.5) are conjugate with respect to the surface (A) and the point A. We mention one property of the parabola (5.14) with respect to the surface (A): If the triangle AMN is inscribed in the parabola (5.14) in a way such that the side MN has an asymptotic direction (6.4), then the straight lines AM and AN are conjugate with respect to the surface (A) and the point A. Indeed, the equation of the straight line MN can be written in the form

$$x^1 + x^2 = h. \tag{6.6}$$

Solving equations (6.6) and (5.14) simultaneously, we obtain

$$x^1 = \frac{h \mp \sqrt{h}}{2}; \quad x^2 = \frac{h \pm \sqrt{h}}{2}. \tag{6.7}$$

If to the upper signs in front of the root correspond the coordinates of the point M, then to the lower signs correspond the coordinates of the point N. The points M and N are real for $h > 0$. In conformity with formulas (5.1–5.2), the vectors

$$\bar{v}_1 = \frac{h - \sqrt{h}}{2}\bar{e}_1 + \frac{h + \sqrt{h}}{2}\bar{e}_2$$

and

$$\bar{v}_1=\frac{h+\sqrt{h}}{2}\bar{e}_1+\frac{h-\sqrt{h}}{2}\bar{e}_2$$

are conjugate.

The equation of the tangent to the parabola (5.14) at the point (x^1, x^2) is

$$(1-2x^1+2x^2)\,y^1+(1+2x^1-2x^2)\,y^2+x^1+x^2=0, \qquad (6.8)$$

where y^1, y^2 are the current coordinates. If the tangent (6.8) is parallel to the Ax^1 axis, then

$$1-2x^1+2x^2=0. \qquad (6.9)$$

From equations (6.9) and (5.14) we can find the coordinates of the point of contact:

$$x^1=\frac{3}{8};\quad x^2=-\frac{1}{8}. \qquad (6.10)$$

The asymptotic direction of the parabola (5.14) coincides with the direction of the straight line on the surface (A) passing through the point A. Indeed, it follows from equations (1.8) and (2.1) that the displacement $d\bar{A}$ for

$$\omega^2=\omega^1$$

takes place along a straight line. It is easy to show that a line with a different asymptotic direction corresponding to

$$\omega^2=-\omega^1,$$

is not straight. Consequently, the straight line part of the indicatrix (5.13) coincides with the straight line on the surface. The tangent to the parabola (5.14) at the point A has a different asymptotic direction (6.4). This follows directly from equation (6.8).

The indicatrix (5.13–5.14) intersects the Ax^1 and Ax^2 axes of the canonical frame at the origin of coordinates and at the unit points of these axes. This also follows directly from equation (5.14).

§ 7. Osculating linear complex of straight lines. A straight line XY passes through the two points XY with homogeneous coordinates (x^0, x^1, x^2, x^3) and (y^0, y^1, y^2, y^3). The six determinants

$$p^{ij}=\begin{vmatrix} x^i & y^i \\ x^j & y^j \end{vmatrix} \qquad (i, j=0, 1, 2, 3) \qquad (7.1)$$

are called the Plücker coordinates of the straight line XY. They are subject to the Plücker condition:

$$p^{01}p^{23}+p^{02}p^{31}+p^{03}p^{12}=0. \qquad (7.2)$$

These coordinates are homogeneous; if we multiply all of them by a nonzero number, we obtain again the Plücker coordinates of the same straight line.

The set of straight lines the Plücker coordinates of which satisfy the equation

$$c_{23}p^{01}+c_{01}p^{23}+c_{31}p^{02}+c_{02}p^{31}+c_{12}p^{03}+c_{03}p^{12}=0 \qquad (7.3)$$

with constant coefficients is called a linear complex of straight lines. The linear complex of straight lines (7.3) is called special if the coefficients of equation (7.3) satisfy the Plücker condition:

$$c_{01}c_{23}+c_{02}c_{31}+c_{03}c_{12}=0. \qquad (7.4)$$

Such a complex represents the set of all straight lines intersecting the straight line the Plücker coordinates of which are $p^{ij} = c_{ij}$. It follows from equation (7.3) that: five straight lines of the linear complex define this complex if their Plücker coordinates satisfy five equations of the form (7.3) and their solutions for c_{ij} have the form $c_{ij} = \lambda c^0_{ij}$, where c^0_{ij} are not all zero (nonzero solution).

Let tangents be drawn to the line l at the point A of the line l and at four infinitely close points of this line.

The linear complex of straight lines defined by these tangents at the limiting position for coincidence of the indicated points with the point A is called the osculating linear complex of straight lines to the line l at the point A. Let us find the osculating linear complex of straight lines with the curved asymptotic line on the surface (A) at the point A. The tangent to this line at the point A contains points the radius vectors of which are $\bar{A}$ and $\bar{A}+\bar{e}_1-\bar{e}_2$ (see § 6).

The Plücker coordinates of this straight line are the determinants of the matrix

$$\|\bar{A},\ \bar{A}+\bar{e}_1-\bar{e}_2\| \text{ or } \|\bar{A},\ \bar{e}_1-\bar{e}_2\|.$$

Therefore the condition that the indicated tangent belong to the complex (7.3) can be written symbolically in the form

$$c\,|\bar{A},\ \bar{e}_1-\bar{e}_2| = 0. \tag{7.5}$$

The required osculating complex of straight lines will be given by the condition (7.5) and four more conditions:

$$cd^m\,|\bar{A},\ \bar{e}_1-\bar{e}_2| = 0 \quad (m = 1, 2, 3, 4). \tag{7.6}$$

Differentiation should correspond to displacement of the point A for

$$\omega^1 + \omega^2 = 0 \tag{7.7}$$

and $d\bar{A}$, $d\bar{e}$ given by equations (2.1).

Differentiating equation (7.5) under condition (7.7), we obtain

$$c\,|\bar{A},\ \bar{e}_1+\bar{e}_2| = 0. \tag{7.8}$$

Differentiating (7.8), simplifying and making use of the condition (7.8), we find that

$$c\,|\bar{e}_1-\bar{e}_2,\ \bar{e}_1+\bar{e}_2| + 2c\,|\bar{A},\ \bar{e}_3| = 0. \tag{7.9}$$

From the above we obtain in the same way

$$2c\,|\bar{e}_1-\bar{e}_2,\ \bar{e}_3| + p_1c\,|\bar{A}\ \bar{e}_1| - p_2c\,|\bar{A}\ \bar{e}_2| = 0. \tag{7.10}$$

Differentiating the above and simplifying, with the aid of (2.1), (7.7–7.10), we obtain

$$\begin{aligned} &4c\,|\bar{e}_1+\bar{e}_2,\ \bar{e}_3| + (p_1-p_2)(5c\,|\bar{e}_1\ \bar{e}_2| + c\,|\bar{A}\ \bar{e}_3|) + \\ &+ [p_1(5q_2-5q_1+2p_1+2p_2+1) - p_2(q_1-q_2-1) + \\ &+ dp_1]\,c\,|\bar{A}\ \bar{e}_1| + [p_2(5q_1-5q_2-2p_1-2p_2+1) + p_1(q_1-q_2+ \\ &+1) - dp_2]\,c\,|\bar{A}\ \bar{e}_2| = 0. \end{aligned} \tag{7.11}$$

To calculate the coefficients c_{ij} of the osculating linear complex we note that the inhomogeneous coordinates $\frac{x^1}{x^0}, \frac{x^2}{x^0}, \frac{x^3}{x^0}$ of the point X with homogeneous coordinates x^0, x^1, x^2, x^3 become respectively equal to the homogeneous coordinates x^1, x^2, x^3 for $x^0 = 1$.

Let us write down the conditions (7.5) and (7.8) in the form (7.3) and the notation (7.1).

We obtain

$$c_{23} = c_{31}, \quad c_{23} + c_{31} = 0.$$

Consequently,

$$c_{23} = 0; \quad c_{31} = 0. \tag{7.12}$$

In exactly the same way, from the conditions (7.9–7.11) we obtain

$$c_{03} + c_{12} = 0; \quad c_{01} + c_{02} = c_{12};$$
$$c_{01} - c_{02} = 5(p_2 - p_1)c_{03} + (p_2 - p_1 - 1)c_{12},$$

or

$$c_{12} = -c_{03}; \quad c_{01} = 2(p_2 - p_1)c_{03}; \quad c_{02} = (2p_1 - 2p_2 - 1)c_{03}. \tag{7.13}$$

For the obtained values of the coefficients (7.12–7.13) and for the condition

$$c_{03} \neq 0 \tag{7.14}$$

the equation of the required osculating linear complex of straight lines is:

$$2(p_2 - p_1)p^{23} + (2p_1 - 2p_2 - 1)p^{31} - p^{03} + p^{12} = 0. \tag{7.15}$$

Replacing the coordinates p^{ij} by their expressions in (7.1), we can write equation (7.15) in the form

$$2(p_2 - p_1)(y^3x^2 - y^2x^3) + (2p_1 - 2p_2 - 1)(y^1x^3 - y^3x^1) +$$
$$+ x^3 - y^3 + y^2x^1 - y^1x^2 = 0. \tag{7.16}$$

If we set in the above

$$y^1 = y^2 = y^3 = 0,$$

then

$$x^3 = 0.$$

This means that the pencil of straight lines of the osculating complex (7.15) which lies in the tangent plane to the surface (A) at the point A passes through the point $A(y^1 = y^2 = y^3 = 0)$. The equations of the straight line tangent to the curved asymptotic line at the point A with reference to the canonical frame are:

$$y^3 = 0; \quad y^1 + y^2 = 0. \tag{7.17}$$

For these conditions equation (7.16) can be written in the form

$$y^1(x^1 + x^2) + (y^1 - 1)x^3 = 0. \tag{7.18}$$

If

$$y^1 = 1, \tag{7.19}$$

then equation (7.18) becomes

$$x^1 + x^2 = 0. \tag{7.20}$$

This means that the point $P(1, -1, 0)$ on the straight line (7.17) is the center of the pencil of straight lines of the complex (7.15) which lies in the plane passing through the normal Ax^3.

§ 8. Geometric interpretation of the choice of canonical frame. The Ax^3 axis of the canonical frame, which is the affine normal to the surface at the point A, contains the centers of the osculating Darboux quadrics (4.1). The tangents to the asymptotic lines at the point A coincide with the tangents to the branches of the line of intersection between the surface (A) and the tangent plane to it at the point A. Their equations with reference to the canonical frame are (6.3) and (6.4). In the definition of conjugate directions (§ 4, Chapter V) an indication is given of a constructive method of obtaining the direction conjugate to a given one.

The geometric methods of obtaining the parabola (5.14), the osculating linear complex of straight lines (7.16), and the point $P(1, -1, 0)$ are well known. We can now regard as known the point $M\left(\frac{1}{2}, -\frac{1}{2}, 0\right)$ – the midpoint of the segment AP– and the straight line passing through the point M parallel to the straight line (6.3). The equation of this straight line is

$$x^1 - x^2 = 1. \tag{8.1}$$

At its intersection with the parabola (5.14), we obtain the point $E_1(1, 0, 0)$, i.e., the unit point on the Ax^1 axis. The straight line AE_1 is the Ax^1 axis. The straight line passing through the point E_1 parallel to the straight line (6.4) intersects the parabola (5.14) at the point $E_2(0, 1, 0)$, i.e., the unit point on the Ax^2 axis. The straight line AE_2 is the Ax^2 axis. If a straight line is drawn through the point E_1 parallel to the Ax^3 axis, then at its intersection with the paraboloid (3.5) we obtain the point $Q\ (1, 0, \frac{1}{2})$. The plane passing through the point R– the endpoint of the segment $E_1R = 2E_1Q$– parallel to the plane x^1Ax^2 intersects the affine normal at the point $E_3\ (0, 0, 1)$, i.e., the unit point on the Ax^3 axis. In addition to a geometric interpretation of the choice of the fundamental points of the canonical frame, we have obtained an interpretation of the choice of the Ax^1 and Ax^2 axes and coordinate lines ω^1 and ω^2.

§ 9. Geometric interpretation of differential invariants. The geometric interpretation of the choice of fundamental points of the canonical frame (§ 8) can be used for a geometric interpretation of all the differential invariants p_1, p_2, q_1, q_2 of the system of Darboux-Cartan equations (2.1). If $d\overline{A}$ is the vector of infinitesimal displacement of the point A along the normal section (n) of the surface (A), $d_c\overline{A}$ is a vector conjugate to the vector $d\overline{A}$ with respect to the surface (A) and the point A, and through every point A of the line (n) there passes a plane given by the equation (5.4), then the characteristic of the family of such planes corresponding to the points of the lines (n) is defined by equations (5.4) and (5.9). Replacing the functions λ_i^j by the forms ω_i^j ((5.2–5.3), Chapter VI) and the forms ω_i^j by their expressions in

(2.1), the equations can be written as

$$
\left.\begin{array}{c}
\omega^1 x^1 - \omega^2 x^2 = 0, \\
\left\{\left[(6q_1 - 2p_1 - 1)\omega^1 + (6q_2 + 2p_2 + 1)\omega^2\right] + (\omega^1 - \omega^2)\omega^2\right\} x^1 + \\
+ \left\{(\omega^1 - \omega^2)\omega^1 + \left[(6q_1 - 2p_1 - 1)\omega^1 + \right.\right. \\
\left.\left. + (6q_2 + 2p_2 + 1)\omega^2\right]\omega^2\right\} x^2 + \left[\omega^2\left(\frac{p_1 - p_2}{2}\omega^1 + p_2\omega^2\right) - \right. \\
\left. - \omega^1\left(p_1\omega^1 + \frac{p_2 - p_1}{2}\omega^2\right)\right] x^3 = \omega^{1^2} - \omega^{2^2}.
\end{array}\right\} \quad (9.1)
$$

Setting here $\omega^2 = 0$, we obtain

$$x^1 = 0, \; x^2 - p_1 x^3 = 1. \quad (9.2)$$

The invariant p_1 can be interpreted geometrically as follows: if the point A describes the normal section of the surface (A) by the plane E_1AE^3, then the planes x^2Ax^3 of the canonical frames $(Ax^1x^2x^3)$ referred to this surface and to the points of the indicated section form a family of planes; the characteristic of this family on the plane E_2AE_3 intersects the AE_2 axis at the unit point E_2 and the AE_3 axis at the point with coordinates $\left(0, 0, -\frac{1}{p_1}\right)$. Consequently, a surface for which the invariant $p_1 = 0$ has a characteristic (9.2) corresponding to the point A, parallel to the normal AE_3 and passing through the point E_2. Setting $\omega^1 = 0$ in equations (9.1), we obtain

$$x^2 = 0; \; x^1 - p_2 x^3 = 1. \quad (9.3)$$

This means that if the point A describes the normal section of the surface (A) by the plane E_2AE_3, then the planes x^1Ax^3 of the canonical frames $(Ax^1x^2x^3)$ referred to this surface and to the points of the indicated section form a family of planes; the characteristic of this family on the plane E_1AE_3 intersects the AE_1 axis at the unit point E_1 and the AE_3 axis at a point with coordinates $\left(0, 0, -\frac{1}{p_2}\right)$. For $p_2 = 0$ this characteristic of the surface is parallel to the normal AE_3 and passes through the unit point E_1.

To interpret the geometric meaning of the invariant q_2, we will consider the ruled surface formed by the tangents to the lines of the family ω^1 at points of the line ω^2 passing through the point A. If there exists a point on the straight line AE_1 with radius vector $\bar{A} + k\bar{e}_1$ such that, for displacement of the point A along the line ω^2,

$$d\left(\bar{A} + k\bar{e}_1\right)_{\omega^1 = 0} = \lambda\bar{e}_1, \quad (9.4)$$

then this point belongs to the edge of regression of the surface formed by the indicated tangents.

Differentiating the left-hand side of equation (9.4), replacing the forms ω_i^k by their expressions in (2.1) and requiring (9.4), we obtain the value of $k = k_1$ for which

$$q_2 = \frac{1}{2} - \frac{1}{k_1}. \quad (9.5)$$

This relation defines the geometric meaning of the invariant q_2. Consequently, if the invariant $q_2 = \frac{1}{2}$ at all points of the surface, then the straight lines passing through points of the line ω^2 and tangent to lines of the family ω^1 constitute a cylindrical surface. In exactly the same way, for the condition

$$\left(d\bar{A} + k\bar{e}_2\right)_{\omega^2 = 0} = \lambda\bar{e}_2,$$

we obtain

$$q_1 = \frac{1}{2} - \frac{1}{k_2},$$

where $\bar{A} - k_2\bar{e}_2$ is the radius vector of the point of contact between the straight line AE_2 and the edge of regression of the developable surface of which the generators are the tangents to the lines of the family ω^2 at points of the line ω^1.

For $q_1 = \frac{1}{2}$, these developable surfaces are cylindrical at all points of the surface.

Chapter XI

CERTAIN LINES ON A RULED SURFACE

§ 1. Canonical frames of the surface and lines on it. Equations (2.1) of Chapter X express the conditions for infinitesimal displacements of the fundamental points of the chosen canonical frame of the surface. Let $(A, \bar{u}_1, \bar{u}_2, \bar{u}_3)$ be the canonical frame of a line belonging to this surface. The Frenet equations corresponding to this line ((14.1), Chapter VIII) are:

$$\left.\begin{aligned} &\frac{d\bar{A}}{d\sigma} = \bar{u}_1; \quad \frac{d\bar{u}_1}{d\sigma} = k_1\bar{u}_1 + \bar{u}_2; \quad \frac{d\bar{u}_2}{d\sigma} = \varepsilon\bar{u}_1 + 2k_1\bar{u}_2 + \bar{u}_3; \\ &\frac{d\bar{u}_3}{d\sigma} = k_2\bar{u}_1 + 3\varepsilon\bar{u}_2 + 3k_1\bar{u}_3. \end{aligned}\right\} \tag{1.1}$$

For displacement of the point A along the same line, if the parameter σ is assumed to be the same, equations (2.1) of Chapter X can be written in the form

$$\left.\begin{aligned} &\frac{d\bar{A}}{d\sigma} = \lambda^1\bar{e}_1 + \lambda^2\bar{e}_2; \\ &\frac{d\bar{e}_1}{d\sigma} = \left[\left(3q_1 - p_1 + \frac{1}{2}\right)\lambda^1 + \left(3q_2 + p_2 - \frac{1}{2}\right)\lambda^2\right]\bar{e}_1 + \\ &\quad + \left[\left(q_1 + \frac{1}{2}\right)\lambda^1 + \left(q_2 - \frac{1}{2}\right)\lambda^2\right]\bar{e}_2 + \lambda^1\bar{e}_4; \\ &\frac{d\bar{e}_2}{d\sigma} = \left[\left(q_1 - \frac{1}{2}\right)\lambda^1 + \left(q_2 + \frac{1}{2}\lambda^2\right]\bar{e}_1 + \\ &\quad + \left[\left(3q_1 - p_1 - \frac{1}{2}\right)\lambda^1 + \left(3q_2 + p_2 + \frac{1}{2}\right)\lambda^2\right]\bar{e}_2 - \lambda^2\bar{e}_3; \\ &\frac{d\bar{e}_3}{d\sigma} = \left(p_1\lambda^1 + \frac{p_2 - p_1}{2}\lambda^2\right)\bar{e}_1 + \\ &\quad + \left(\frac{p_1 - p_2}{2}\lambda^1 + p_2\lambda^2\right)\bar{e}_2 + \left[\left(6q_1 - 2p_1\right)\lambda^1 + \right. \\ &\quad \left. + \left(6q_2 + 2p_2\right)\lambda^2\right]\bar{e}_3. \end{aligned}\right\} \tag{1.2}$$

The relation between the frame $(A, \bar{u}_1, \bar{u}_2, \bar{u}_3)$ and the frame $(A, \bar{e}_1, \bar{e}_2, \bar{e}_3)$ can be expressed in the form

$$\left.\begin{aligned} \bar{u}_1 &= \lambda^1\bar{e}_1 + \lambda^2\bar{e}_2; \\ \bar{u}_2 &= a^1\bar{e}_1 + a^2\bar{e}_2 + (\lambda^{1^2} - \lambda^{2^2})\,\bar{e}_3; \\ \bar{u}_3 &= b^1\bar{e}_1 + b^2\bar{e}_2 + b^3\bar{e}_3, \end{aligned}\right\} \tag{1.3}$$

where

$$\left.\begin{aligned} a^1 &= \frac{d\lambda^1}{d\sigma} + \lambda^1\lambda_1^1 + \lambda^2\lambda_2^1 - k_1\lambda^1; \\ a^2 &= \frac{d\lambda^2}{d\sigma} + \lambda^1\lambda_1^2 + \lambda^2\lambda_2^2 - k_1\lambda^2; \\ b^1 &= \frac{da^1}{d\sigma} + a^1\lambda_1^1 + a^2\lambda_2^1 + (\lambda^{1^2} - \lambda^{2^2})\,\lambda_3^1 - \varepsilon\lambda^1 - 2k_1a^1; \\ b^2 &= \frac{da^2}{d\sigma} + a^1\lambda_1^2 + a^2\lambda_2^2 + (\lambda^{1^2} - \lambda^{2^2})\,\lambda_3^2 - \varepsilon\lambda^2 - 2k_1a^2; \\ b^3 &= \frac{d(\lambda^{1^2} - \lambda^{2^2})}{d\sigma} + a^1\lambda^1 - a^2\lambda^2 + \\ &\quad + (\lambda^{1^2} - \lambda^{2^2})\,\lambda_3^3 - 2k_1(\lambda^{1^2} - \lambda^{2^2}); \\ &\frac{db^1}{d\sigma} + b^1\lambda_1^1 + b^2\lambda_2^1 + b^3\lambda_3^1 = k_2\lambda^1 + 3\varepsilon a^1 + 3k_1b^1; \\ &\frac{db^2}{d\sigma} + b^1\lambda_1^2 + b^2\lambda_2^2 + b^3\lambda_3^2 = k_2\lambda^2 + 3\varepsilon a^2 + 3k_1b^2; \\ &\frac{db^3}{d\sigma} + b^1\lambda^1 - b^2\lambda^2 + b^3\lambda_3^3 = 3\varepsilon(\lambda^{1^2} - \lambda^{2^2}) + 3k_1b^3. \end{aligned}\right\} \tag{1.4}$$

The relation between the differential invariants of the surface and the skew line in the form (1.3–1.4) contains the condition that this line can be placed on the surface.

If the line on the surface is plane and $(A, \bar{v}_1, \bar{v}_2)$ is its canonical frame, then the corresponding Frenet formulas ((6.1), Chapter XI) are:

$$\frac{d\bar{A}}{d\sigma} = \bar{v}_1, \quad \frac{d\bar{v}_1}{d\sigma} = k\bar{v}_1 + \bar{v}_2, \quad \frac{d\bar{v}_2}{d\sigma} = \varepsilon\,\bar{v}_1 + 2k\bar{v}_2. \tag{1.5}$$

In the same way as for the (skew) line, let us find the equations that express the relation between the frame $(A, \bar{v}_1, \bar{v}_2)$ and the canonical frame of the surface $(A, \bar{e}_1, \bar{e}_2, \bar{e}_3)$. We will also assume that

$$\bar{v}_1 = \lambda^\alpha\bar{e}_\alpha \quad (\alpha, \beta, \gamma = 1, 2). \tag{1.6}$$

Differentiating the above, we obtain

$$\frac{d\bar{v}_1}{d\sigma} = \left(\frac{d\lambda^\alpha}{d\sigma} + \lambda^\beta\lambda_\beta^\alpha\right)\bar{e}_\alpha + \lambda^\beta\lambda_\beta^3\,\bar{e}_3. \tag{1.7}$$

If the plane line is a normal section, then equation (1.7) can be written in the form

$$\frac{d\bar{v}_1}{d\sigma} = \varphi\bar{v}_1 + \lambda^\beta\lambda_\beta^3\bar{e}_3, \tag{1.8}$$

where

$$\frac{d\lambda^\alpha}{d\sigma} + \lambda^\beta\lambda_\beta^\alpha = \varphi\lambda^\alpha. \tag{1.9}$$

From equations (1.8) and (1.5 : 2), the vector of the normal to the plane section at the point A is:

$$\bar{v}_2 = (\varphi - k)\bar{v}_1 + \lambda^{\beta}\lambda^{3}_{\beta}\bar{e}_3. \tag{1.10}$$

For displacement of the point A in the normal section, the vector $d\bar{e}_3$ does not in general remain in the plane of this section. The projection of the vector $d\bar{e}_3$ onto the indicated plane parallel to the vector ((5.2), Chapter XI)

$$d_c\bar{A} = \omega^2\bar{e}_1 + \omega^1\bar{e}_2,$$

which is conjugate to the vector $d\bar{A}$ can be obtained from the expansion

$$d\bar{e}_3 = \lambda\omega^{\alpha}\bar{e}_{\alpha} + \omega^{3}_{3}\bar{e}_3 + \mu(\omega^2\bar{e}_1 + \omega^1\bar{e}_2)$$

in the form

$$d_1\bar{e}_3 = \lambda\,\omega^{\alpha}\bar{e}_{\alpha} + \omega^{3}_{3}\bar{e}_3 = \frac{\omega^1\omega^{1}_{3} - \omega^2\omega^{2}_{3}}{\omega^{1^2} - \omega^{2^2}}\,\omega^{\alpha}\bar{e}_{\alpha} + \omega^{3}_{3}\bar{e}_3. \tag{1.11}$$

The symbol d_1 will denote differentiation in which the differential of the vector $\bar{e}_3$ is defined by formula (1.11). Differentiating equation (1.10) in this manner, we obtain

$$\left.\begin{aligned} &\frac{d(\varphi - k)}{d\sigma} + (\varphi - k)(\varphi - 2k) + \lambda^1\lambda^{1}_{3} - \lambda^2\lambda^{2}_{3} = \varepsilon,\\ &\frac{d\lambda^{\beta}\lambda^{3}_{\beta}}{d\sigma} + \lambda^{\beta}\lambda^{3}_{\beta}\left(\lambda^{3}_{3} + \varphi - 3k\right) = 0. \end{aligned}\right\} \tag{1.12}$$

From equations (1.12 : 2), (1.9) and (1.2) we have

$$\varphi - k = \frac{(\lambda^1 - \lambda^2)^2}{3(\lambda^1 + \lambda^2)}. \tag{1.13}$$

Formula (1.10) can now be written in the form

$$\bar{v}_2 = \frac{(\lambda^1 - \lambda^2)^2}{3(\lambda^1 + \lambda^2)}\bar{v}_1 + \left(\lambda^{1^2} - \lambda^{2^2}\right)\bar{e}_3. \tag{1.14}$$

Equations (1.6) and (1.14) define the relation between the canonical frame $(A, \bar{v}_1, \bar{v}_2)$ of the normal section and the canonical frame of the surface.

§ 2. Normal sections of the surface. The vector of the normal $\bar{v}_2$ to the normal section will be defined in the canonical frame of the surface $(A, \bar{e}_1, \bar{e}_2, \bar{e}_3)$ if we replace the vector $\bar{v}_1$ in formula (1.14) by its expansion in (1.6):

$$\bar{v}_2 = \frac{(\lambda^1 - \lambda^2)^2}{3(\lambda^1 + \lambda^2)}\lambda^{\alpha}\bar{e}_{\alpha} + \left(\lambda^{1^2} - \lambda^{2^2}\right)\bar{e}_3. \tag{2.1}$$

The equation of the normal to the normal section can be written in the form

$$\bar{X} = \bar{A} + \rho\bar{v}_2, \tag{2.2}$$

where $\bar{X}$ is the radius vector of the generic point of the straight line.

If $\bar{X} = x^i\bar{e}_i$, then equation (2.2) can be replaced by equations with reference to the frame $(A, \bar{e}_1, \bar{e}_2, \bar{e}_3)$:

$$x^1 = \rho\frac{(\lambda^1 - \lambda^2)^2}{3(\lambda^1 + \lambda^2)}\lambda^1;\quad x^2 = \rho\frac{(\lambda^1 - \lambda^2)^2}{3(\lambda^1 + \lambda^2)}\lambda^2;\quad x^3 = \rho\left(\lambda^{1^2} - \lambda^{2^2}\right). \tag{2.3}$$

The equation of this conical surface in implicit form is

$$3(x^1 + x^2)^2 - x^3(x^1 + x^2) = 0. \tag{2.4}$$

The planes of the bundle with its axis normal to the ruled surface form normal sections of this surface with the normals belonging to the cone of second order (2.4).

At the intersection between this cone and the plane specified by the equation

$$x^3 = 1, \tag{2.5}$$

we obtain a parabola (Figure 5) the projection of which parallel to the Ax^3 axis onto the E_1AE_2 plane is given by the equation

$$3(x^1 + x^2)^2 - x^1 + x^2 = 0. \tag{2.6}$$

In conformity with formula (2.1) and equation (2.6), the normal sections the planes of which contain asymptotic directions do not have affine normals at the point A.

§ 3. Lines with osculating planes normal to the surface. The osculating plane of the line on the surface (A) at the point A contains the vectors $\bar{u}_1$ and $\bar{u}_2$ (§ 1). Therefore the condition that this plane pass through the normal to the surface (A) is:

$$|\,\bar{u}_1 \;\; \bar{u}_2 \;\; \bar{e}_3\,| = 0. \tag{3.1}$$

Replacing $\bar{u}_1$ and $\bar{u}_2$ by their expressions in (1.3) and $\lambda_i^j\, d\sigma$ by the forms ω_i^j, we obtain the differential equation of lines the osculating planes of which are normal to the surface:

$$\omega^2 d\omega^1 - \omega^1 d\omega^2 + \omega^1\omega^2\left(\omega_1^1 - \omega_2^2\right) + \omega^{2^2}\omega_2^1 - \omega^{1^2}\omega_1^2 = 0. \tag{3.2}$$

The forms ω_i^k are defined by the choice of canonical frame in equations (2.1) of Chapter X. Therefore equation (3.2) can be written in the form

$$\omega^2 d\omega^1 - \omega^1 d\omega^2 - \frac{1}{2}\left(\omega^1 - \omega^2\right)^3 + \left(\omega^{2^2} - \omega^{1^2}\right)\left(q_1\omega^1 + q_2\omega^2\right) = 0. \tag{3.3}$$

Lines on the surface the osculating planes of which are normal to the surface are defined only by the invariants q_1 and q_2.

§ 4. Lines with principal normals normal to the surface. It follows from (1.3) that the condition which defines such lines is

$$\bar{u}_2 = \left(\lambda^{1^2} - \lambda^{2^2}\right)\bar{e}_3. \tag{4.1}$$

Consequently, an asymptotic line cannot be a line at points of which the principal normal coincides with the normal to the surface.

For the condition (4.1), it follows from (1.3 : 2) that

$$a^1 = 0;\; a^2 = 0. \tag{4.2}$$

Replacing a^1 and a^2 by their expressions in (4.1) and $\lambda_i^k\, d\sigma$ by the forms ω_i^k we obtain the differential equations of the lines under consideration:

$$\frac{d\omega^1 + \omega^1\omega_1^1 + \omega^2\omega_2^1}{\omega^1} = \frac{d\omega^2 + \omega^1\omega_1^2 + \omega^2\omega_2^2}{\omega^2} = k_1, \tag{4.3}$$

where k_1 is the first curvature of the line at the point A. The expression for the curvature k_1 is the same in these equations as in (8.5), Chapter VIII, but the forms ω_i^k are those in (2.1), Chapter X.

For the condition (4.2), we obtain

$$\left.\begin{aligned} b^\alpha &= \left(\lambda^{1^2} - \lambda^{1^2}\right)\lambda_3^\alpha - \varepsilon\lambda^\alpha \quad (\alpha = 1,\ 2);\\ b^3 &= \frac{d\left(\lambda^{1^2} - \lambda^{2^2}\right)}{d\sigma} + \left(\lambda^{1^2} - \lambda^{2^2}\right)\left(\lambda_3^3 - 2k_1\right). \end{aligned}\right\} \tag{4.4}$$

This means that a curved asymptotic line of a ruled surface cannot be a line on which the principal normal coincides with the normal to the surface. It follows immediately that the vector $\overline{u}_2$ at points of an asymptotic line should be tangent to the surface.

§ 5. **Lines of curvature.** It follows from equation (6.1) of Chapter VIII that the equation of such lines is

$$\omega^1\omega_3^2 - \omega^2\omega_3^1 = 0.$$

Replacing the forms ω_3^1 and ω_3^2 by their expressions in (2.1), Chapter X, we obtain

$$(p_1 - p_2)(\omega^1 - \omega^2)^2 = 0. \tag{5.1}$$

The only lines of curvature of a ruled surface with $p_1 \neq p_2$ are the generators of this surface $\omega^1 = \omega^2$; if the invariants $p_1 = p_2$ are equal, then any line on the surface is a line of curvature.

In the former case the radius vector of the focus F of the normal is

$$\overline{F} = \overline{A} - \frac{2}{p_1 + p_2}\overline{e}_3, \tag{5.2}$$

in the latter case

$$\overline{F} = \overline{A} - \frac{1}{p_1}\overline{e}_3. \tag{5.3}$$

§ 6. **Darboux lines.** The equation of the three-parameter family of osculating quadrics (7.8), Chapter VI, for the values (1.3), Chapter VI, is

$$x^{1^2} - x^{2^2} - 2x^3 + \frac{b_1}{2}x^1x^3 + \frac{b_2}{2}x^2x^3 + A_{33}x^{3^2} = 0. \tag{6.1}$$

The equation of the surface (A) in implicit form ((3.6), Chapter X) is

$$2x^3 = x^{1^2} - x^{2^2} - \frac{1}{3}(x^1 - x^2)^2 + 0(4). \tag{6.2}$$

Eliminating x^3 from equations (6.1) and (6.2), we obtain the condition imposed on the coordinates x^1 and x^2 of the line of intersection of these surfaces and simultaneously the equation of the projection of this line onto the surface x^1Ax^2 along the direction of the normal Ax^3. In general three branches of this line pass through the origin A.

The condition of osculation of the three branches among themselves at the point A is the identity

$$\left(\frac{1}{3} + \frac{b_1}{4}\right)x^{1^3} + \left(\frac{b_2}{4} - 1\right)x^{1^2}x^2 + \left(1 - \frac{b_1}{4}\right)x^1x^{2^2} - \\ - \left(\frac{1}{3} + \frac{b_2}{4}\right)x^{2^3} \equiv \left(\frac{1}{3} + \frac{b_1}{4}\right)(x^1 + tx^2)^3. \tag{6.3}$$

Consequently,

$$\frac{b_2}{4} - 1 = 3t\left(\frac{1}{3} + \frac{b_1}{4}\right);\ 1 - \frac{b_1}{4} = \left(\frac{1}{3} + \frac{b_1}{4}\right)3t^2; \\ -\frac{1}{3} - \frac{b_2}{4} = \left(\frac{1}{3} + \frac{b_1}{4}\right)t^3. \tag{6.4}$$

The condition of compatibility of the above equations for arbitrary b^1 and b^2 is:

$$13t^3 + 3t^2 + 3t + 13 = 0. \tag{6.5}$$

But

$$13t^3 + 3t^2 + 3t + 13 \equiv (t+1)(13t^2 - 10t + 13).$$

The only real root of equation (6.4) is $t = -1$; the remaining two are conjugate complex. This means that the only real Darboux lines on a skew ruled surface are the generators of this surface, and that, like the asymptotic lines, they coincide with the corresponding Segrè lines.

Chapter XII

CERTAIN RULED SURFACES

§ 1. Affine ruled sphere. If $\overline{A}+\lambda\overline{e}_3$ is the radius vector of the point of intersection of all normals of the surface (A), then

$$d(\overline{A} + \lambda\overline{e}_3) = 0;$$

$$\omega^1 + \lambda\omega_3^1 = 0; \quad \omega^2 + \lambda\omega_3^2 = 0; \tag{1.1}$$

$$\omega_3^3 = 0. \tag{1.2}$$

The condition of compatibility of equations (1.1) for arbitrary λ is:

$$\omega^1\omega_3^2 - \omega^2\omega_3^1 = 0. \tag{1.3}$$

Replacing the forms in equations (1.2–1.3) by their expressions in (2.1), Chapter X, we obtain (see (5.1)):

$$(p_1 - p_2)(\omega^1 - \omega^2)^2 = 0; \quad (3q_1 - p_1)\omega^1 + (3q_2 + p_2)\omega^2 = 0.$$

Consequently, for arbitrary ω^1 and ω^2,

$$p_1 = p_2 = 3q_1 = -3q_2. \tag{1.4}$$

For the condition (1.4), it follows from the equations of structure (2.2) of Chapter XI that

$$p_1 = p_2 = q_1 = q_2 = 0. \tag{1.5}$$

This defines ruled spheres.

§ 2. Surfaces with parallel affine normals. The condition that the vector of the normal $\overline{e}_3$ be parallel to the vector of the normal at any neighboring point is:

$$\overline{e}_3 + d\overline{e}_3 = \lambda\overline{e}_3$$

or

$$\omega_3^\alpha \overline{e}_\alpha = (\lambda - 1 - \omega_3^3)\overline{e}_3 \quad (\alpha = 1, 2).$$

Consequently,

$$\left.\begin{aligned} \omega_3^1 = 0, \quad \omega_3^2 = 0; \\ \lambda - 1 - \omega_3^3 = 0. \end{aligned}\right\} \tag{2.1}$$

Replacing the forms in the above by their expressions in (2.1), Chapter X, we obtain

$$p_1\omega^1 + \frac{p_2 - p_1}{2}\omega^2 = 0; \quad \frac{p_1 - p_2}{2}\omega^1 + p_2\omega^2 = 0$$

which should be identically satisfied for arbitrary ω^1 and ω^2. Therefore

$$p_1 = p_2 = 0. \tag{2.2}$$

For the values of the invariants in (2.2), the normals to the surface are parallel to each other.

§ 3. Surfaces with coplanar normals. If every vector of the normal to the surface $\bar{e}_3$ is coplanar with the fixed noncollinear vectors $\bar{v}_1$ and $\bar{v}_2$, then

$$\bar{e}_3 = \lambda^{\alpha} \bar{v}_{\alpha} \quad (\alpha = 1, 2).$$

Differentiating the above, we obtain

$$(\omega_3^{\alpha} + \omega_3^3 \lambda^{\alpha}) \, \bar{e}_{\alpha} = \bar{v}_{\alpha} d\lambda^{\alpha}. \tag{3.1}$$

Replacing the forms ω_3^i in the above by their expressions in (2.1), Chapter X, we obtain

$$\left\{[p_1 + \lambda^1 (6q_1 - 2p_1)] \, \bar{e}_1 + \left[\frac{p_1 - p_2}{2} + \lambda^2 (6q_1 - 2p_1)\right] \bar{e}_2\right\} \omega^1 +$$

$$+ \left\{\left[\frac{p_2 - p_1}{2} + \lambda^1 (6q_2 + 2p_2)\right] \bar{e}_1 + \left[p_2 + \lambda^2 (6q_2 + 2p_2)\right] \bar{e}_2\right\} \omega^2 =$$

$$= \bar{v}_{\alpha} d\lambda^{\alpha}.$$

The left-hand side of this equation represents the vector coplanar with the vectors $\bar{e}_1$ and $\bar{e}_2$, and the right-hand side, the vector coplanar with the vectors $\bar{v}_1$ and $\bar{v}_2$. In general the tangent planes to the surface (A) are not parallel to the two vectors $\bar{v}_1$ and $\bar{v}_2$. Therefore

$$p_1 + \lambda^1 (6q_1 - 2p_1) = 0, \quad \frac{p_2 - p_1}{2} + \lambda^1 (6q_2 + 2p_2) = 0; \tag{3.2}$$

$$\frac{p_1 - p_2}{2} + \lambda^2 (6q_1 - 2p_1) = 0, \quad p_2 + \lambda^2 (6q_2 + 2p_2) = 0; \tag{3.3}$$

$$d\lambda^{\alpha} = 0. \tag{3.4}$$

The conditions of compatibility of equations (3.2) for arbitrary λ^1 and of equations (3.3) for arbitrary λ^2 are:

$$\left.\begin{aligned} (p_1 - p_2)(3q_1 - p_1) + 2p_1 (3q_2 + p_2) &= 0; \\ 2p_2 (3q_1 - p_1) - (p_1 - p_2)(3q_2 + p_2) &= 0. \end{aligned}\right\} \tag{3.5}$$

To this relation between the differential invariants correspond surfaces with coplanar normals. The requirement (3.5) is fulfilled if

$$3q_1 = p_1; \quad 3q_2 + p_2 = 0. \tag{3.6}$$

If the above condition does not hold, then

$$p_1 + p_2 = 0; \quad p_1 (3q_1 + 3q_2 - 2p_1) = 0. \tag{3.7}$$

To the value $p_1 = 0$ and, therefore $p_2 = 0$ in the above system should correspond surfaces with parallel normals (§ 2). Excluding this case in the system (3.7), we obtain

$$p_1 + p_2 = 0; \quad 3q_1 + 3q_2 = 2p_1. \tag{3.8}$$

To the condition (3.6), as well as to (3.8), correspond surfaces with coplanar normals. Under condition (3.6) an infinitesimal displacement of the unit point E_3 along the normal is parallel to the tangent plane at the point where this normal is drawn to the surface.

§ 4. Examples and problems. 1. Examples of geometrical interpretation of certain functions of the invariants of the surface.

a) The tangent to the line (E_1) at the unit point E_1 for motion of the point A along the line ω^1 intersects the plane passing through the unit point E_3 parallel to the tangent plane x^1Ax^2 at a point with the coordinates

$$x^1 = 3q_1 - p_1 + \frac{5}{2}; \quad x^2 = q_1 + \frac{1}{2}; \quad x^3 = 1.$$

In all the examples the coordinates are local with reference to the canonical frame.

b) The tangent to the line (E_1) for motion of the point A along the line ω^2 lies in the plane x^1Ax^2 and intersects the Ax^2 axis at the point

$$x^1 = 0; \; x^2 = \frac{2q_2 - 1}{1 - 6q_2 - 2p_2}; \; x^3 = 0.$$

c) If the point A describes the generator of the surface, then the tangent to the line (E_1) at the point E_1 intersects the plane passing through the point E_3 parallel to the plane x^1Ax^2 at the point

$$x^1 = 1 + 3(q_1 + q_2) + p_2 - p_1; \; x^2 = q_1 + q_2; \; x^3 = 1.$$

d) If the point A describes the line ω^1, then the tangent to the line (E_3) at the point E_3 intersects the tangent plane x^1Ax^2 at the point

$$x^1 = \frac{p_2}{2p_1 - 6q_2}; \quad x^2 = \frac{p_1 - p_2}{4(p_1 - 3q_2)}; \quad x^3 = 0.$$

2. a) The characteristic of the family of osculating paraboloids

$$2x^3 = x^{1^2} - x^{2^2} \tag{4.1}$$

is the intersection of the surface (4.1) and the surface

$$\omega^1 x^1 - \omega^2 x^2 + \omega_3^3 x^3 - \omega_1^1 x^{1^2} + \left(\omega_1^2 - \omega_2^1\right) x^1 x^2 + \omega_2^2 x^{2^2} -$$
$$- \omega_3^1 x^1 x^3 + \omega_3^2 x^2 x^3 = 0.$$

b) If the point A moves along the generator of the surface, then the characteristic of this family on the surface (4.1) decomposes into the line of intersection of the paraboloid (4.1) with the plane and with the cylinder

$$x^1 = x^2; \quad x^{1^2} - x^{2^2} = \frac{4}{p_1 + p_2}.$$

c) Give the geometrical interpretation of the invariant $\frac{4}{p_1 + p_2}$.

3. a) At the points of a curved asymptotic line the normal planes to the surface that are osculating with this line form the family the characteristic of which is the straight line of intersection of the planes

$$\left.\begin{aligned} x^1 + x^2 = 0; \; (8q_1 + 8q_2 + 3p_2 - 3p_1)\, x^1 + \\ + (8q_1 + 4q_2 + 3p_2 - 3p_1)\, x^2 + (p_1 + p_2)\, x^3 = 2. \end{aligned}\right\} \tag{4.2}$$

b) The plane (4.2 : 2) intersects the rectilinear generator of the surface which passes through the point A at the point

$$x^1 = \frac{1}{2q_2}; \quad x^2 = -\frac{1}{2q_2}; \quad x^3 = 0.$$

Give the geometrical interpretation of the invariant q_2.

4. a) If the point A moves along the normal section of the surface in the plane

$$x^1 = 0, \tag{4.3}$$

then the characteristic of the family of such planes corresponding to the points of the given section is the intersection of the plane (4.3) and the plane

$$x^2 - p_1 x^3 = 1.$$

Give the geometrical interpretation of the invariant p_1.

b) If the point A moves along the normal section in the plane

$$x^2 = 0, \tag{4.4}$$

then the characteristic of the family of such planes corresponding to the points of the normal section is the intersection of the plane (4.4) and the plane

$$x^1 - p_2 x^3 = 1.$$

Give the geometrical interpretation of the invariant p_2.

5. If the invariants p_1 and p_2 of a ruled surface satisfy the condition

$$p_1 + p_2 = 0,$$

then the normals to this surface at the points of each of its generators are parallel to each other, while if $p_1 \neq 0$ then, apart from these lines, there are no other lines with this property.

6. On a ruled surface with invariants satisfying the condition

$$4(1+p_1)(1+p_2) = (p_1 - p_2)^2,$$

at the points of every line of the family

$$2(1+p_1)\,\omega^1 + (p_2 - p_1)\,\omega^2 = 0$$

the normals to the surface intersect at the unit point E_3.

7. The ruled surface given by the equations (5.9), Chapter X, decomposes into a plane and a cone of the second order

$$x^1 = x^2; \quad (x^1 - x^2)^2 + (p_2 x^1 + p_1 x^2)\,x^3 = 0.$$

Give the geometric interpretation of the invariants p_1 and p_2.

8. The characteristics of the family of normal planes at points of the curved asymptotic line that passes through the generators of this surface constitute a surface the generators of which are parallel to the corresponding generators of the given surface.

9. A skew ruled surface intersects the tangent plane to it, to infinitesimals of the fourth order, along a line of the third order which decomposes into a straight line and a parabola

$$x^1 = x^2; \quad (x^1 - x^2)^2 = 3(x^1 + x^2).$$

10. One can choose the canonical frame $(A, \bar{e}_1, \bar{e}_2, \bar{e}_3)$ with reference to a surface such that the vectors $\bar{e}_1$ and $\bar{e}_2$ have asymptotic directions and the equations for infinitesimal displacements of this frame are

$$d\bar{A} = \omega^1 \bar{e}_1 + \omega^2 \bar{e}_2;$$

$$d\bar{e}_1 = -[(2p_1 + p_4)\,\omega^1 + (2p_2 + p_5)\,\omega^2]\,\bar{e}_1 + \omega^1 \bar{e}_2 + \omega^2 \bar{e}_3;$$

$$d\bar{e}_2 = \omega^2 \bar{e}_1 - [(p_1 + 2p_4)\,\omega^1 + (p_2 + 2p_5)\,\omega^2]\,\bar{e}_2 + \omega^1 \bar{e}_3;$$

$$d\bar{e}_3 = (p_3\omega^1 + 3p_1\omega^2)\,\bar{e}_1 + (3p_2\omega^1 + p_3\omega^2)\,\bar{e}_2 - 3\,[(p_1 + p_4)\,\omega^1 + (p_2 + p_5)\,\omega^2]\,\bar{e}_3.$$

Write down the corresponding structure equations. Interpret the geometrical relation between the frame and the surface.

Chapter XIII

CONCERNING THE EXISTENCE OF CERTAIN SURFACES

§ 1. Surfaces with all differential invariants constant. Unruled surfaces with all differential invariants constant exist if these invariants p_1, p_2, p_3, q_1, q_2 satisfy the equations of structure (9.2) of Chapter V in the form

$$\left.\begin{aligned} & 2p_2q_1 + q_2(p_1 - p_3) = 0; \\ & p_1^2 + 4\alpha p_2^2 + p_3^2 - 2q_1^2 - 2\alpha q_2^2 - 2p_2q_2 - \alpha q_1p_3 + \alpha p_1q_1 - 2p_1p_3 - \\ & \quad - \frac{9}{2}\alpha(p_1 + p_3) = 0; \\ & \alpha q_2 - p_2 + \frac{5}{3}p_1q_2 - \frac{4}{3}\alpha p_1p_2 + \frac{4}{3}\alpha p_2p_3 - \frac{4}{3}p_2q_1 + \\ & \quad + \frac{1}{3}p_3q_2 = 0; \\ & \frac{4}{3}\alpha p_2q_2 - \frac{4}{3}p_2^2 + \frac{1}{2}p_3 - \frac{1}{2}p_1 - \alpha q_1 + \frac{\alpha}{3}p_3^2 - \\ & \quad - \frac{2}{3}\alpha p_1p_3 - \frac{5}{3}p_3q_1 - \frac{p_1}{3}(q_1 - \alpha p_1) = 0. \end{aligned}\right\} \tag{1.1}$$

The Pfaffian system of equations (9.1) of Chapter V is completely integrable here. Its solution depends on the arbitrarily specified frame $(A, \bar{e}_1, \bar{e}_2, \bar{e}_3)$. If u^1, u^2 are independent variables and (du_1, du^2) is the basis of the ring equivalent to the basis (ω^1, ω^2), then to the fixed point (u_0^1, u_0^2) and corresponding fixed frame $(A, \bar{e}_1, \bar{e}_2, \bar{e}_3)$ correspond the unique solution of the system (9.1), Chapter V, and the unique surface (§ 7, Chapter I). To integrate the system (9.1), Chapter V, one can set

$$\omega^1 = a_1^1 du^1; \quad \omega^2 = a_2^2 du^2, \tag{1.2}$$

where a_1^1, a_2^2 are functions u^1, u^2 satisfying the equations

$$\left.\begin{aligned} & \frac{da_1^1}{du^2} + \frac{2}{3}(q_2 - \alpha p_2)a_1^1a_2^2 = 0; \\ & \frac{da_2^2}{du^1} + \frac{1}{3}(2q_1 + \alpha p_1 - \alpha p_3)a_1^1a_2^2 = 0, \end{aligned}\right\} \tag{1.3}$$

in conformity with the requirement (9.2 : 1−2) of Chapter V. For the chosen expressions of ω^1 and ω^2, the lines ω^1 coincide with the lines du^1 and the lines ω^2 with the lines du^2. For brevity we set

$$\left.\begin{aligned} & D\omega^1 \equiv b^1[\omega^1\omega^2]; \quad D\omega^2 = b^2[\omega^1\omega^2]; \\ & b^1 = \frac{2}{3}(q_2 - \alpha p_2); \; b^2 = \frac{1}{3}(\alpha p_3 - \alpha p_1 - 2q_1). \end{aligned}\right\} \tag{1.4}$$

Therefore equation (1.3) can be written in the form

$$\frac{da_1^1}{du^2} + b^1a_1^1a_2^2 = 0; \quad \frac{da_2^2}{du^1} - b^2a_1^1a_2^2 = 0. \tag{1.5}$$

To integrate equations (9.1) of Chapter V, it is necessary to know the functions a_1^1 and a_2^2. If we restrict ourselves to the case where these functions are assured of existence but may be specified arbitrarily, then with (1.5) we can write

$$\left.\begin{aligned} da_1^1 &= p\,du^1 - b^1 a_1^1 a_2^2\,du^2; \\ da_2^2 &= b^2 a_1^1 a_2^2\,du^1 + q\,du^2. \end{aligned}\right\} \tag{1.6}$$

In this Pfaffian system u^1, u^2 are independent variables and a_1^1, a_2^2, p, q are unknown functions.

Exterior differentiation of equations (1.6) gives

$$\left.\begin{aligned} [dp + b^1 a_2^2 (b^2 a_1^{1^2} + p)\,du^2,\ du^1] &= 0; \\ [b^2 a_1^1 (b^1 a_2^{2^2} - q)\,du^1 + dq,\ du^2] &= 0. \end{aligned}\right\} \tag{1.7}$$

If n is the number of independent variables, r is the number of unknown functions, s is the number of linearly independent Pfaffian equations, s_1, s_2 are the characters of the system, Q is Cartan's number and N is the number of parametric functions of the system (1.6), then (cf. Chapter I) we have:

$$n = 2;\ s = 2;\ r = 4;\ s_1 = 2;\ s_2 = 0;\ Q = 2;\ N = 2.$$

The last value is obtained because, from (1.7),

$$dp + b^1 a_2^2 (b^2 a_1^{1^2} + p)\,du^2 = \alpha\,du^1;$$

$$b^2 a_1^1 (b^1 a_2^{2^2} - q)\,du^1 + dq = \beta\,du^2,$$

where α, β are two parametric functions.

The system (1.6) is involutive. The required functions a_1^1, a_2^2 and p, q exist, but are arbitrary up to two functions of one argument. Explicit expressions can be obtained for a_1^1, a_2^2.

We introduce the new symbols:

$$a_1^1 = z;\ u^1 = x;\ u^2 = y. \tag{1.8}$$

In the new notation we obtain from (1.5)

$$\frac{d^2 z}{dx\,dy} = b^2 z \frac{dz}{dy} + \frac{1}{z}\frac{dz}{dx}\frac{dz}{dy}. \tag{1.9}$$

Let the number $b^2 \neq 0$. Equation (1.9) can be written in the form

$$\frac{d}{dy}\left(\frac{1}{z}\frac{dz}{dx}\right) = \frac{d}{dy}(b^2 z).$$

Therefore

$$\frac{1}{z}\frac{dz}{dx} = b^2 z + \varphi, \tag{1.10}$$

where φ is an arbitrary function of x. The above equation is a Bernoulli equation. Therefore we can write

$$z = \frac{e^{\int \varphi dx}}{\psi - b^2 \int e^{\int \varphi dx} dx}, \tag{1.11}$$

where ψ is an arbitrary function of y.

Returning to the earlier notation, we obtain

$$a_1^1 = \frac{e^{\int \varphi du^1}}{\psi - b^2 \int e^{\int \varphi du^1} du^1}, \tag{1.12}$$

where φ is an arbitrary function of u^1 and ψ an arbitrary function of u^2. Now an explicit expression for a_2^2 can be found from equation (1.5 : 1).

Ruled surfaces with all invariants p_1, p_2, q_1, q_2 constant exist if these invariants satisfy the equations of structure (2.2) of Chapter X in the form

$$\left.\begin{aligned} &3q_2^2 - 3q_1^2 + p_1q_1 + p_2q_2 = 0;\\ &q_2^2 - q_1^2 + p_1q_2 + p_2q_1 - \frac{1}{2}p_1 - \frac{1}{2}p_2 = 0;\\ &(p_2 - p_1)(p_1 - 2q_1 + q_2) + 2p_1(p_2 + 3q_2) = 0;\\ &(p_1 - p_2)(p_2 - q_1 + 2q_2) + 2p_2(p_1 - 3q_1) = 0 \end{aligned}\right\} \tag{1.13}$$

and

$$D\omega^1 = (p_2 - q_1 + 3q_2)[\omega^1\omega^2]; \quad D\omega^2 = (p_1 - 3q_1 + q_2)[\omega^1\omega^2]. \tag{1.14}$$

The introduction of the curvilinear coordinates u^1, u^2 on the surface and of the coordinate lines coinciding with the lines ω^1, ω^2 follows in the same way as in equation (1.2), the only difference being that here

$$b^1 = p_2 - q_1 + 3q_2; \quad b_2 = p_1 - 3q_1 + q_2. \tag{1.15}$$

§ 2. Unruled surfaces for which $p_2=0, p_3=p_1$. To such surfaces (affine spheres, (§ 2, Chapter IX) correspond the equations of structure (9.2) of Chapter V, which can be reduced to the form

$$\left.\begin{aligned} &dp_1 = (\alpha + p_1)(q_1\omega^1 + q_2\omega^2);\\ &[dq_1\omega^1] + [dq_2\omega^2] = 0;\\ &[dq_2\omega^1] - \alpha[dq_1\omega^2] + \frac{1}{3}(9p_1 - 2\alpha q_1^2 + 2q_2^2)[\omega^1\omega^2] = 0. \end{aligned}\right\} \tag{2.1}$$

In this system of exterior differential equations, the forms ω^1, ω^2 are linearly independent, p_1, q_1, q_2 are unknown functions and the quantities n, s, r, s_1, s_2, Q defined in § 1 have the following values: $n=2$; $s=1$; $s_1=2$; $s_2=0$; $Q=2$. From equation (2.1 : 2) we obtain by Cartan's lemma

$$dq_1 = a\omega^1 + b\omega^2; \quad dq_2 = b\omega^1 + c\omega^2. \tag{2.2}$$

Replacing dq_1, dq_2 in (2.1 : 3) by their expressions in (2.2), we obtain

$$b = 3p_1 + \frac{2}{3}(q_2^2 - \alpha q_1^2) - \alpha a.$$

Therefore among the functions a, b, c the number of parametric functions $N=2$. The system (2.1) is involutive; its integral manifold (M_2) exists with an arbitrariness of two functions of one argument. If such functions p_1, q_1, q_2 and $p_2=0$, $p_3=p_1$ appear in equations (9.1) of Chapter V, then the latter form a completely integrable system and its integral manifold will again be arbitrary up to the constants. Therefore the maximum arbitrariness is that of two functions of one argument.

§ 3. Unruled surfaces with parallel normals. To such surfaces (§ 3, Chapter X) correspond the values of the invariants

$$p_2 = 0;\ p_1 = -\frac{a}{2} = p_3.$$

The equations of structure (9.2) of Chapter V can be written in the form

$$\left.\begin{aligned} &[dq_1\omega^1] + [dq_2\omega^2] = 0; \\ &[dq_2\omega^1] - a\,[dq_1\omega^2] + \frac{1}{3}(2aq_1^2 + 2q_2^2 - \frac{9}{2}a)\,[\omega^1\omega^2] = 0. \end{aligned}\right\} \qquad (3.1)$$

Here ω^1, ω^2 are linearly independent forms, q_1, q_2 are the required functions, $n = 2$; $s = 0$; $r = 2$; $s_1 = 2$; $s_2 = 0$; $Q=2$. From equation (3.1 : 1) we obtain by Cartan's lemma

$$dq_1 = a\omega^1 + b\omega^2;\ dq_2 = b\omega^1 + c\omega^2. \qquad (3.2)$$

Replacing dq_1 and dq_2 in equation (3.1 : 2) by their expressions in equation (3.2), we obtain

$$c = \frac{1}{3}\left(2aq_1^2 + 2q_2^2 - \frac{9}{2}a\right)aa.$$

The number of parametric functions among a, b is $N=2$. The system (3.1) is involutive. The integral manifold M_2 of the system (3.1) exists with an arbitrariness of two functions of one argument.

§ 4. Ruled surfaces with parallel normals. To these surfaces correspond the values of the invariants (§ 2, Chapter XII)

$$p_1 = p_2 = 0. \qquad (4.1)$$

For the condition (5.1), the equations of structure (2.2), Chapter X, degenerate into one equation

$$[dq_1\omega^1] + [dq_2\omega^2] + (q_2^2 - q_1^2)\,[\omega^1\omega^2] = 0. \qquad (4.2)$$

Here ω^1, ω^2 are linearly independent forms on the integral manifold of equation (5.2); q_1, q_2 are unknown functions; $n = 2$; $s = 0$; $s_1 = 1$. But since $r - s = s_1 + s_2$, $s_2 = 1$. Cartan's number $Q = s_1 + 2s_2 = 3$.

From equation (5.2) we obtain by Cartan's lemma

$$dq_1 = a\omega^1 + b\omega^2;\ dq_2 = b\omega^1 + c\omega^2.$$

All the functions a, b, c are parametric; $N=3$. Equation (4.2) is involutive; its integral manifold exists with an arbitrariness of one function of two arguments.

The indicated arbitrariness is maximal for integration of the completely integrable system (2.1), Chapter X, with the condition (4.1) and with the functions q_1, q_2 satisfying equation (4.2). Ruled surfaces with parallel normals exist with an arbitrariness of one function of two arguments.

BIBLIOGRAPHY

1. BLASCHKE, W. Vorlesungen über Differentialgeometrie und geometrische Grundlagen von Einsteins Relativitätstheorie, Band 2, Berlin. 1923.

2. NORDEN, A. P. Prostranstva affinnoi svyaznosti (Affinely-Connected Spaces). Moskva-Leningrad. 1950.

3. SHIROKOV, P. A. and A. P. SHIROKOVA. Affinnaya differentsial'naya geometriya (Affine Differential Geometry). Moskva. 1959.

4. SHCHERBAKOV, R. N. Spetsial'nyi kurs affinnoi differentsialnoi geometrii (Special Course in Affine Differential Geometry). Manuscript, Tomsk. 1959.

5. SHCHERBAKOV, R. N. Kurs affinnoi i proektivnoi differentsial'noi geometrii (Course in Affine and Projective Differential Geometry). Tomsk. 1960.

6. FINIKOV, S. P. Metod vneshnikh form Kartana v differentsial'noi geometrii (Cartan's Method of Exterior Forms in Differential Geometry). Moskva-Leningrad. 1948.

7. FINIKOV, S. P. Teoriya par kongruentsii (Theory of Pairs of Congruences). Moskva. 1956.

8. LAPTEV, G. F. Differentsial'naya geometriya pogruzhennykh mnogoobrazii (Differential Geometry of Embedded Manifolds). – Trudy Moskovskogo Matematicheskogo Obshchestva, Vol. 2, Moskva. 1953.